PUPIL TEXTBOOK

6A

Noogol

Googol

Koogol

Ooogol.

Toogol

Zoogol

Consultant and author
Dr Fong Ho Kheong

Authors
Gan Kee Soon and Chelvi Ramakrishnan

UK consultants
Carole Skinner, Simon d'Angelo and Elizabeth Gibbs

Introduction

Inspire Maths is a comprehensive, activity-based programme designed to provide pupils with a firm foundation in maths and to develop creative and critical thinking skills to become fluent problem solvers.

Inspire Maths makes learning maths fun and rewarding through the use of engaging illustrations and games that help to reinforce and consolidate learning.

For the teacher:

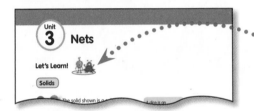

Use the engaging and highly scaffolded **Let's Learn!** to introduce concepts. Integrated questions allow for immediate assessment and consolidation of concepts learnt.

Carry out investigative activities in **Let's Explore!** These allow pupils to apply concepts learnt.

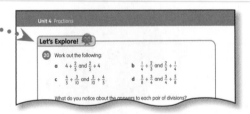

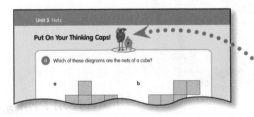

Challenge pupils to solve non-routine questions by applying relevant heuristics and thinking skills in **Put On Your Thinking Caps!**

Indicates that appropriate use of calculators is encouraged for the activities and practices to extend problem-solving skills.

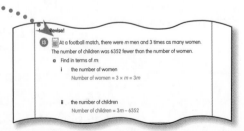

For the parent/guardian:

Build home-school links and make maths come alive by using the tips in Home Maths to help children apply mathematical concepts to daily life.

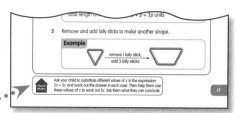

For the pupil:

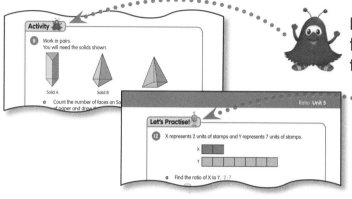

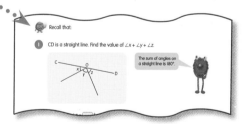

Enjoy **Inspire Maths** with your friends. Explore your learning through activities and group work.

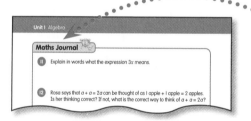

Let's Practise! contains questions that provide opportunities for further practice.

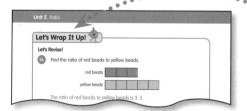

Share what you have learnt, create your own questions and become aware of your own mathematical thinking in your **Maths Journal**.

Recall skills from earlier years and link them to new concepts in the current unit.

Let's Wrap It Up! summarises the concepts you have learnt in the current unit, while **Let's Revise!** provides a worked example that covers the key concepts for ease of revision.

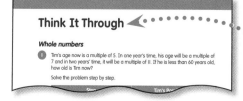

Use the worked examples and questions to help you understand problem-solving strategies.

Contents

Let's Learn!

Using letters as numbers

1 Millie is now 11 years old.

a How old will Millie be in 1 year's time?

11 + 1 = 12

Millie will be 12 years old in 1 year's time.

b How old will Millie be in 2 years' time?

11 + 2 = 13

Millie will be 13 years old in 2 years' time.

c How old was Millie 1 year ago?

11 − 1 = 10

Millie was 10 years old 1 year ago.

d How old was Millie 2 years ago?

11 − 2 = 9

Millie was 9 years old 2 years ago.

2   Mr Green is a class teacher.
Mr Green's class do not know how old he is.

Mr Green is x years old.

In algebra, we use a letter to represent an **unknown number**.

If Mr Green is 47 years old, then x represents 47.

If Mr Green is 38 years old, then x represents 38.

a   How old will Mr Green be in I year's time?

$x + 1$

Mr Green will be $(x + 1)$ years old in I year's time.

b   How old will Mr Green be in 2 years' time?

$x + 2$

Mr Green will be $(x + 2)$ years old in 2 years' time.

$x + 1$ and $x + 2$ are examples of **algebraic expressions** in terms of x.

3   Refer to the table below. What is Mr Green's age in terms of x?

	Mr Green's Age (Years)
Now	x
In 3 years' time	⬭
In 4 years' time	⬭
In 7 years' time	⬭
In 10 years' time	⬭
In 15 years' time	⬭

4 Mrs Smith is the headteacher of Greentree Primary School.
The pupils do not know her age.

Mrs Smith is y years old.

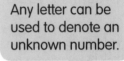

Any letter can be used to denote an unknown number.

a How old was Mrs Smith 1 year ago?

$y - 1$

Mrs Smith was $(y - 1)$ years old 1 year ago.

b How old was Mrs Smith 2 years ago?

$y - 2$

Mrs Smith was $(y - 2)$ years old 2 years ago.

$y - 1$ and $y - 2$ are examples of algebraic expressions in terms of y.

5 Refer to the table below. What is Mrs Smith's age in terms of y?

	Mrs Smith's Age (Years)
Now	y
3 years ago	⬚
5 years ago	⬚
8 years ago	⬚
12 years ago	⬚
20 years ago	⬚

6 **a** **i** Add 2 to 6.

$6 + 2 = 8$

ii Add x to 6.

$6 + x$

b **i** Subtract 3 from 4.

$4 - 3 = 1$

ii Subtract 3 from y.

$y - 3$

c　**i**　What is 4 more than 8?　**ii**　What is x more than 8?

$8 + 4 = 12$　　　　　　　　$8 + x$

d　**i**　What is 5 less than 9?　**ii**　What is 5 less than y?

$9 - 5 = 4$　　　　　　　　$y - 5$

7　State the algebraic expression for each of the following.

a　Add 5 to z 　　　　　　　　**b**　Add z to 8

c　Subtract 7 from z 　　　　　**d**　Subtract z from 10

e　9 more than z 　　　　　　　**f**　z more than 9

g　11 less than z 　　　　　　　**h**　z less than 11

8　Find the values of the algebraic expressions by using the numbers given below.

a　Find the value of $x + 5$ when $x = 9$.

When $x = 9$,
$x + 5 = 9 + 5$
　　　$= 14$

Substitute the letter with the given number.

b　Find the value of $5 + x$ when $x = 23$.

When $x = 23$,
$5 + x = 5 + 23$
　　　$= 28$

c　Find the value of $y - 7$ when $y = 15$.

When $y = 15$,
$y - 7 = 15 - 7$
　　　$= 8$

d　Find the value of $30 - y$ when $y = 7$.

When $y = 7$,
$30 - y = 30 - 7$
　　　$= 23$

9 Refer to the table below. Find the values of the algebraic expressions for the given values of x.

Expression	Value of Expression When:	
	$x = 8$	$x = 30$
$x + 4$	$8 + 4 = 12$	$30 + 4 = 34$
$x + 9$		
$12 + x$		
$x - 3$		
$x - 6$		
$40 - x$		

10 There are 12 pencils in a box.

a How many pencils are there in 2 boxes?

$2 \times 12 = 24$

There are 24 pencils in 2 boxes.

b How many pencils are there in 3 boxes?

$3 \times 12 = 36$

There are 36 pencils in 3 boxes.

11 There are n pencils in a box.

a How many pencils are there in 2 boxes?

$2 \times n = 2n$

There are $2n$ pencils in 2 boxes.

b How many pencils are there in 3 boxes?

$3 \times n = 3n$

There are $3n$ pencils in 3 boxes.

We write $2 \times n$ as $2n$ and $3 \times n$ as $3n$.

2*n* and 3*n* are examples of algebraic expressions in terms of *n*.

1 × *n* or *n* × 1 is equal to *n*.

3*n* is 3 × *n* or 3 groups of *n*.

12*p* is 12 × *p* or *p* × 12.

12 Answer these questions.

a $4k = \boxed{} \times \boxed{}$

b $7j = \boxed{} \times \boxed{}$

c 5*p* means $\boxed{}$ groups of $\boxed{}$.

d 8 groups of *x* is $\boxed{} \times \boxed{}$.

13 Refer to the table below. There are *n* marbles in a packet. Find the number of marbles in terms of *n*. Then find the number of marbles for the given values of *n*.

Number of Packets	Number of Marbles	Number of Marbles When:	
		n = 15	*n* = 20
1	*n*	15	20
4	4*n*	4 × 15 = 60	$\boxed{}$
7	$\boxed{}$	$\boxed{}$	$\boxed{}$
10	$\boxed{}$	$\boxed{}$	$\boxed{}$
15	$\boxed{}$	$\boxed{}$	$\boxed{}$

14 There are 6 cartons of juice in a pack.

a If the cartons of juice are shared equally between 2 children, how many cartons will each child get?

$6 \div 2 = 3$

Each child will get 3 cartons.

b If the cartons of juice are shared equally between 3 children, how many cartons will each child get?

$6 \div 3 = 2$

Each child will get 2 cartons.

15 There are m cartons of juice in a pack.

a If the cartons of juice are shared equally between 2 children, how many cartons will each child get?

$m \div 2 = \dfrac{m}{2}$

Each child will get $\dfrac{m}{2}$ cartons.

We write $m \div 2$ as $\dfrac{m}{2}$.

b If the cartons of juice are shared equally among 3 children, how many cartons will each child get?

$m \div 3 = \dfrac{m}{3}$

Each child will get $\dfrac{m}{3}$ cartons.

We write $m \div 3$ as $\dfrac{m}{3}$.

$\dfrac{m}{2}$ and $\dfrac{m}{3}$ are also algebraic expressions.

$\dfrac{m}{1}$ is equal to m.

$\dfrac{p}{6}$ means $p \div 6$.

16 Refer to the table below. A packet of *m* stickers is shared equally among some children. Find the number of stickers each child gets in terms of *m*. Then find the number of stickers for the given values of *m*.

Number of Children	Number of Stickers Each Child Gets	Number of Stickers Each Child Gets When:	
		m = 24	*m* = 48
1	*m*	24	48
3	$\frac{m}{3}$	$\frac{24}{3} = 8$	
6			
8			
12			

17 Refer to the questions below. Find the expressions in terms of *p*. For the boxes on the right, find the value when *p* = 6. The first one has been done for you.

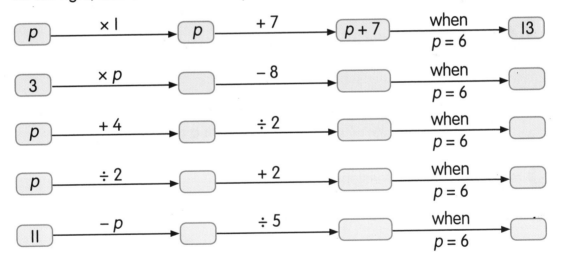

18 Find the value of each expression when *a* = 20.

a $10a - 89$

b $\frac{125 - a}{7}$

c $\frac{11a}{4} + 25$

d $\frac{14a + 80}{30}$

Home Maths

Discuss with your child what the letter *x* means in these expressions:
$x + 6$, $6 - x$, $6x$ and $\frac{x}{6}$. Explain that *x* stands for an unknown number.

Activity

19 Work in pairs.
You will need 5 letter cards and 5 number cards.

I Pick one letter card and one number card.

2 Write down as many algebraic expressions as you can with the two cards. For example, if you pick the cards x and 8, you can write down '$x + 8$', '$8 + x$', '$x - 8$', '$8 - x$', '$8x$' and '$\dfrac{x}{8}$'.

3 Repeat steps I and 2 until all the cards have been taken.

Let's Explore!

20 Look at these expressions:

a $\dfrac{y}{2}$
b $\dfrac{1}{2} \times y$

Find the values of the expressions in **a** and **b** when:

i $y = 6$
ii $y = 14$

Choose 3 other values of y and work out the values of the expressions in **a** and **b** above. What do you notice about **a** and **b**?

21 Look at these expressions:

a $\dfrac{y - 2}{3}$
b $(y - 2) \div 3$
c $\dfrac{1}{3} \times (y - 2)$

Find the values of the expressions in **a**, **b** and **c** when:

i $y = 8$
ii $y = 17$

Choose any other 3 values of y and work out **a**, **b** and **c** above. What do you conclude about **a**, **b** and **c**?

22 Express $(x + 4) \div 6$ in two other ways.

Maths Journal

23 Write two story number sentences that have the following expressions as answers.

    a $m - 20$ **b** $5m$

Let's Practise!

24 Express each of the following in one or two other ways.

    a $5 \times w$ **b** $v \times 15$

    c $x \div 3$ **d** $\frac{1}{4} \times y$

    e $\frac{z + 4}{5}$ **f** $\frac{1}{2} \times (a - 7)$

25 John is now x years old. Give an expression in terms of x for each of the following and find the value when $x = 18$.

    a   The age of his brother, who is 5 years older than him.

    b   The age of his sister, who is 3 years younger than him.

    c   The age of his aunt, who is twice as old as him.

    d   The age of his cousin, who is half his age.

26 There are n pieces of chocolate in a box. Give an expression in terms of n for each of the following and find the value when $n = 24$.

    a   The number of pieces of chocolate left after 6 pieces have been eaten.

    b   The number of pieces of chocolate each child gets when the box of chocolate is shared equally among 4 children.

    c   The total number of pieces of chocolate in 10 identical boxes.

    d   The number of pieces each child gets when one box and 11 pieces of chocolate are shared equally among 5 children.

Let's Practise!

27 Give the expression for each of the following.

    a   Add *b* to 9   **b**   Subtract 4 from *b*

    c   Subtract *b* from 10   **d**   Multiply *b* by 3

    e   Multiply 7 by *b*   **f**   Divide *b* by 5

    g   Half of *b*   **h**   Add 10 to *b*

    i   Subtract *b* from 11   **j**   Multiply *b* by 6

28 In the following part-whole models, find the missing expressions. Then use your calculator to find the value of each expression when *y* = 36.

    a

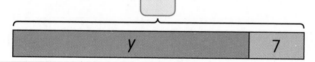

    b

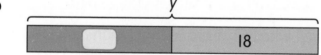

    c

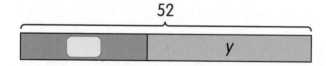

    d

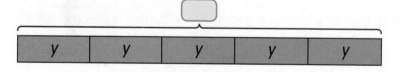

    e

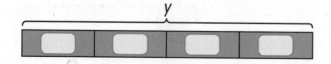

Practice Book 6A, p.1

12

Let's Learn!

Simplifying algebraic expressions

1

a cm a cm

A rod of length a cm is joined to another rod also a cm long. What is the total length of the 2 rods?

Total length of the 2 rods = $(a + a)$ cm

$(a + a)$ is also $(2 \times a)$.

We can simplify $(a + a)$ by writing:

$a + a = 2a$

| 3 | 3 |

$3 + 3 = 2 \times 3$

| 4 | 4 |

$4 + 4 = 2 \times 4$

| a | a |

$a + a = 2 \times a$

2 The diagram below is made up of 3 rods, each b cm long. Find the total length of the 3 rods.

b cm b cm b cm

Total length = $b + b + b$
$\qquad\qquad = (3 \times b)$ cm

We can simplify $(b + b + b)$ by writing:

$b + b + b = 3b$

| 5 | 5 | 5 |

$5 + 5 + 5 = 3 \times 5$

| b | b | b |

$b + b + b = 3 \times b$

3 The diagram below is made up of 5 sticks, each *r* cm long. What is the total length of the 5 sticks?

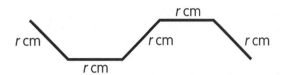

r cm

r cm   *r* cm   *r* cm

r cm

r r r r r

$r + r + r + r + r = 5 \times r$

Total length = $r + r + r + r + r$
$= 5 \times r$
$= 5r$ cm

4 Simplify these expressions.

a $x + x$

b $y + y + y$

c $a + a + a + a + a$

d $b + b + b + b + b + b$

e $c + c + c + c + c + c + c$

5 Simplify $a + 2a$.

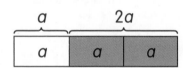

a $2a$

a a a

$a + 2a = a + a + a$
$= 3a$

$a + 2a = 3a$

6 Simplify $2a + 3a$.

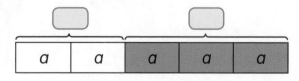

a a a a a

$2a + 3a = \boxed{} + \boxed{} + \boxed{} + \boxed{} + \boxed{}$
$= \boxed{}$

7 Simplify these expressions.

a $a + 3a$ **b** $2z + 5z$ **c** $4x + x$

d $3y + 6y$ **e** $b + 2b + 3b$ **f** $4c + 2c + 5c$

8 A ribbon is a cm long. Peter uses the whole ribbon to decorate a present. How much ribbon is left?

Length of ribbon left $= a - a$
$ = 0$ cm

Compare the following:
$2 - 2 = 0$
$7 - 7 = 0$
$a - a = 0$

9 Find the value of:

a $x - x$ **b** $2y - 2y$ **c** $10z - 10z$

10 Simplify $3a - a$.

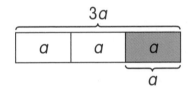

$3a$

| a | a | a |

a

$3a - a = a + a$
$ = 2a$

$3a - a = 2a$

11 Simplify $4a - 2a$.

$4a$

| a | a | a | a |

$2a$

$4a - 2a = a + a$
$ = 2a$

$4a - 2a = 2a$

12 Simplify $5a - 2a$.

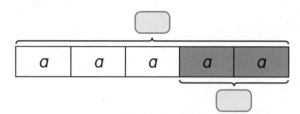

$5a - 2a = \boxed{} + \boxed{} + \boxed{}$

$ = \boxed{}$

13 Simplify these expressions.

a $4a - a$ **b** $7a - 3a$ **c** $5x - 4x$

d $10x - 6x$ **e** $8y - 3y - 5y$ **f** $12y - 7y - y$

14 Simplify $6a + 3a - 2a$.

Working from left to right,

$6a + 3a - 2a = 9a - 2a$

$ = 7a$

15 Simplify $6a - 2a + 3a$.

Working from left to right,

$6a - 2a + 3a = 4a + 3a$

$ = 7a$

16 Find the distance from Point A to Point B.

	a km	4 km	a km	2 km	
A					**B**

Total distance $= a + 4 + a + 2$

$ = a + a + 4 + 2$

$ = (2a + 6)$ km

Compare this with:
$2 + 3 + 4 = 3 + 2 + 4$

17 Simplify $4x + 6 - 2x$.

$$4x + 6 - 2x = 4x - 2x + 6$$
$$= 2x + 6$$

18 Simplify these expressions.

a $2x + 3x - 4x$ **b** $x + 5x - 6x$

c $9a - 3a + 4a$ **d** $12a - 7a + 2a$

e $b + 5 + b + 5$ **f** $3b + 4b + 2 + 6$

g $5s + 9 - 3s$ **h** $8s + 6 - 2s - 1$

Activity

19 Work in pairs.
You will need 20 lolly sticks.
Take the length of each lolly stick as p units.

I Make a closed shape using 3 or more lolly sticks.

> **Example**
>
>

2 Write down the total length of the lolly sticks used.

> **Example**
>
> Total length of lolly sticks $= p + p + p = 3p$ units

3 Remove and add lolly sticks to make another shape.

> **Example**
>
>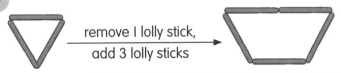
>
> remove I lolly stick, add 3 lolly sticks

Ask your child to substitute different values of x in the expression
$2x + 3x$ and work out the answer in each case. Then help them use
these values of x to work out $5x$. Ask them what they can conclude.

Home Maths

Activity

4   Write down the total length of the lolly sticks used in the new shape by subtracting the total length of the lolly sticks removed and adding the total length of the lolly sticks added.

> ### Example
>
> When one lolly stick was removed and three lolly sticks were added:
> Total length of lolly sticks = $3p - p + 3p$
> = $5p$ units

5   Check your answer in **4** by counting the number of lolly sticks used in the new shape to find the total length.

> ### Example
>
> Total number of lolly sticks used = 5
> Total length of lolly sticks = $5 \times p$
> = $5p$ units

6   Make other shapes and repeat the exercise.

Let's Practise!

20   Simplify these expressions.

a	$2a + 5a$	**b**	$a + 7a$
c	$3a + 3a + 6a$	**d**	$4x - 2x$
e	$6x - 5x$	**f**	$10x - 2x - 8x$
g	$7y - 5y + 4y$	**h**	$9y + 3y - 5y$
i	$a + a + 5$	**j**	$b + 4 + 4 + b$
k	$2s + 7 - 6 + s$	**l**	$9r + 10 + 2 - 3r$

Practice Book 6A, p.9

Let's Learn!

Word problems

1 Matt has *y* computer games. Anna has 3 times as many computer games as Matt. Anna buys another 7 computer games.

    a How many more computer games does Anna have than Matt after she buys another 7 computer games, in terms of *y*?

    b If Matt has 25 computer games, how many more computer games does Anna have than Matt?

    a Anna has $(3y + 7)$ computer games.
       $3y + 7 - y = 2y + 7$

       Anna has $(2y + 7)$ more computer games than Matt.

    b $2y + 7 = (2 \times 25) + 7$
                $= 50 + 7$
                $= 57$

       Anna has 57 more computer games than Matt.

2 Sophie has £*m* and Ahmed has £15 more.

    a Find the amount of money they have altogether in terms of *m*.

    b If Sophie has £75, how much money do they have altogether?

    a Ahmed has £ (⬚).
       They have £ (⬚) altogether.

    b If $m = 75$, they have £⬚ altogether.

3 Alisha had £x in her purse. She bought a book for £15 and spent the rest of her money on 3 theatre tickets.

    a   Find the price of 1 theatre ticket in terms of x.

    b   If Alisha had £39, what was the price of 1 theatre ticket?

    a   Price of 3 theatre tickets = £$(x - 15)$

$$£(x - 15) \div 3 = £\left(\frac{x - 15}{3}\right)$$

         The price of 1 theatre ticket is £$\left(\frac{x - 15}{3}\right)$.

    b $£\left(\dfrac{x - 15}{3}\right) = £\left(\dfrac{39 - 15}{3}\right)$

$$= £\left(\frac{24}{3}\right)$$

$$= £8$$

         The price of 1 theatre ticket was £8.

4 Mr Elliott had £y in his wallet. He earned £200 and then spent half the total amount of money on sport equipment.

    a   Find the amount of money he had left in terms of y.

    b   If $y = 80$, how much money did he have left?

    a   Total amount of money he had = £(⬚)

         Mr Elliott had £(⬚) left.

    b   If $y = 80$, he had £⬚ left.

Let's Practise!

Solve these word problems. Show your workings clearly.

5 Harry is r years old. His brother is 3 times as old as he is. His sister is 4 years younger than his brother.

    a   Find his brother's age in terms of r.

    b   Find his sister's age in terms of r.

    c   If $r = 5$, how old is his sister?

Let's Practise!

6 Mr Davis bought a belt for £x and some shoes that cost twice as much as the belt. He gave the sales assistant £100.

    a Find the amount that Mr Davis spent in terms of x.

    b Find the amount of change Mr Davis received in terms of x.

    c If $x = 15$, how much change did Mr Davis receive?

7 Daniel scored z marks in a maths test. Kerry scored 4 times as many marks. Rajesh scored 5 more marks than Kerry.

    a Find the marks that Kerry scored in terms of z.

    b Find the marks that Rajesh scored in terms of z.

    c Find the total marks scored by the three pupils in terms of z.

8 At a concert, there were t men and twice as many women. During the interval, 5 men and 6 women left the concert.

    a How many people left during the interval?

    b How many people were there at the concert after the interval?

    c If $t = 500$, how many people were there at the concert after the interval?

9 Mrs Brook had some blackberries. She packed 14 blackberries into each bag. There were m bags of blackberries altogether. The blackberries were shared equally among her 3 children.

    a How many blackberries did each child get? Give your answer in terms of m.

    b If there were 18 bags of blackberries, how many blackberries did each child get?

10 A full bucket and a full jug contain $p\,\ell$ of water altogether. The bucket contains 10 times as much water as the jug.

    a Find the amount of water in the jug in terms of p.

    b If the full bucket and the full jug contain $25\,\ell$ of water altogether, find the amount of water in the bucket in litres to 1 decimal place.

Practice Book 6A, p.11

21

Maths Journal

11 Explain in words what the expression $3x$ means.

12 Rosa says that $a + a = 2a$ can be thought of as 1 apple + 1 apple = 2 apples. Is her thinking correct? If not, what is the correct way to think of $a + a = 2a$?

Let's Wrap It Up!

You have learnt:

- that letters in algebra stand for numbers
- to write and evaluate algebraic expressions
- to simplify algebraic expressions.

Let's Revise!

13 At a football match, there were m men and 3 times as many women.

The number of children was 6352 fewer than the number of women.

a Find in terms of m:

i the number of women

Number of women = $3 \times m = 3m$

ii the number of children

Number of children = $3m - 6352$

Let's Wrap It Up!

iii   the number of men and women.

Number of men and women = $m + 3m = 4m$

b   If $m = 7145$, how many people were there at the football match?

Total number of people = $4m + 3m - 6352$
$$= 7m - 6352$$
$$= 7 \times 7145 - 6352$$
$$= 43\,663$$

There were 43 663 people at the football match.

Put On Your Thinking Caps!

14   Abby thinks of a number. First she multiplies it by 2. She then adds 12 to the result. Finally she takes the result and subtracts twice the original number. What answer will she always get?

Practice Book 6A, p.19   Practice Book 6A, p.20

Unit 2 Angles in Shapes and Diagrams

Let's Learn!

 Recall that:

1 CD is a straight line. Find the value of $\angle x + \angle y + \angle z$.

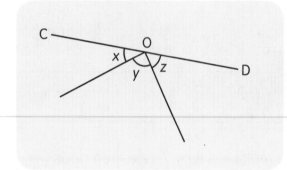

The sum of angles on a straight line is 180°.

$$\angle x + \angle y + \angle z = \boxed{}°$$

2 Find the value of $\angle w + \angle x + \angle y + \angle z$.

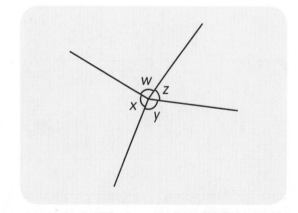

The sum of angles at a point is 360°.

$$\angle w + \angle x + \angle y + \angle z = \boxed{}°$$

3 AB and CD are straight lines.

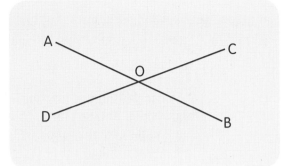

$\angle$AOC = $\angle$ ⬡

$\angle$BOC = $\angle$ ⬡

Vertically opposite angles are equal.

Practice Book 6A, p.21

4 ABC is a triangle.

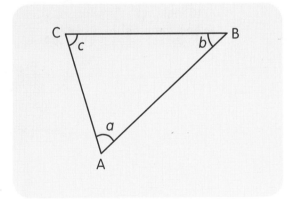

The sum of the angles in a triangle is 180°.

$\angle a + \angle b + \angle c =$ ⬡ °

5 ABC is an isosceles triangle with AB = AC.

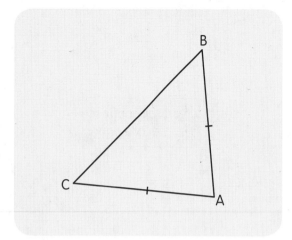

An isosceles triangle has two equal sides. The angles opposite the equal sides are equal.

∠☐ = ∠☐

6 ABC is an equilateral triangle.

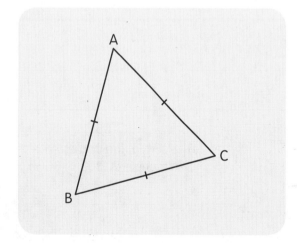

An equilateral triangle is a triangle with three equal sides and three equal angles.

∠ABC = ∠☐ = ∠☐ = ☐°

7 EFGH is a rhombus and WXYZ is a parallelogram.

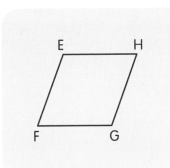

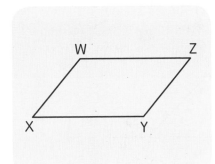

There are two pairs of parallel lines.

EF = ⬚ = ⬚ = ⬚   WZ = ⬚ and WX = ⬚

∠EFG = ∠⬚   ∠WXY = ∠⬚

∠HEF = ∠⬚   ∠XYZ = ∠⬚

∠HEF + ∠EFG = ⬚°   ∠WXY + ∠XYZ = ⬚°

∠EFG + ∠FGH = ⬚°   ∠ZWX + ∠WXY = ⬚°

8 STUV is a trapezium where SV // TU.

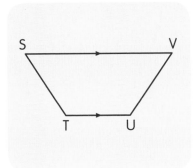

∠TUV and ∠UVS are a pair of angles between two parallel sides.

∠TUV + ∠UVS = ⬚°

∠VST + ∠STU = ⬚°

9 The diagram below is not drawn to scale. ABC is an isosceles triangle in which AB = AC. BD is a straight line. Find ∠ACB and ∠ABC.

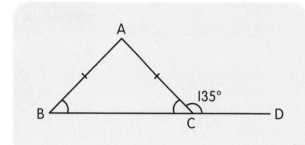

∠ACB = 180° − 135°
    = 45°

∠ABC = ∠ACB = 45°

Angles on a straight line...

Angles opposite the equal sides of an isosceles triangle...

10 The diagram below is not drawn to scale. ZW is a straight line and XYZ is an isosceles triangle in which XY = XZ. Find ∠YXZ and ∠YXW.

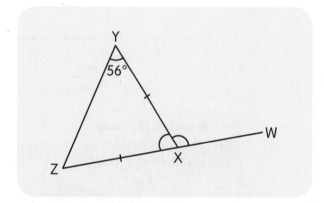

∠XZY = ∠☐ = ☐°

∠YXZ = ☐° − ☐° − ☐°
    = ☐°

∠YXW = ☐° − ☐°
    = ☐°

Practice Book 6A, p.23

11 The diagram below is not drawn to scale. ABC is a triangle. AD and AE are straight lines. Find $\angle$ABC and $\angle$CBD.

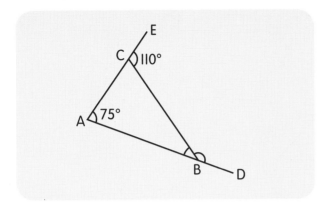

$\angle$ACB = 180° − 110°
       = 70°

$\angle$ABC = 180° − 75° − 70°
       = 35°

$\angle$CBD = 180° − 35°
       = 145°

Angles on a straight line...

Sum of angles in a triangle...

Angles on a straight line...

12 The shape below is not drawn to scale. BD is a straight line and ACD is an isosceles triangle where AC = AD. Find $\angle$ACB and $\angle$CAB.

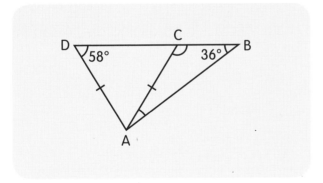

$\angle$ACD = ⬚°

$\angle$ACB = ⬚° − ⬚° = ⬚°

$\angle$CAB = ⬚° − ⬚° − ⬚°

       = ⬚°

13 The shape below is not drawn to scale. ABCD is a parallelogram. BE and CE are straight lines. Find ∠EDF and ∠BEC.

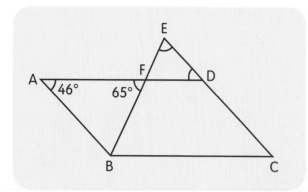

∠ADC = 180° − 46°
  = 134°

∠EDF = 180° − 134°
  = 46°

∠EFD = 65°

∠BEC = 180° − 46° − 65°
  = 69°

Angles between two parallel sides AB and DC...

Angles on a straight line...

Vertically opposite angles...

Sum of angles in a triangle...

14 The shape below is not drawn to scale. ABCD is a parallelogram. AF and BF are straight lines. Find ∠AED and ∠CFE.

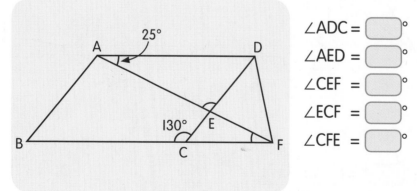

∠ADC = ☐°
∠AED = ☐°
∠CEF = ☐°
∠ECF = ☐°
∠CFE = ☐°

Activity

15 Work in pairs.
Look at the 7 statements in the box below.

1 Read the first statement. Then draw a shape that fits the description.

2 Read the second statement and redraw your shape accordingly.

3 Continue redrawing your shape, if necessary, after each of the remaining statements.

4 After the last statement, compare the shape you have drawn with the shape your partner has drawn.

> **i** The shape has 4 sides.
>
> **ii** One pair of the opposite sides is parallel.
>
> **iii** The other pair of opposite sides is equal.
>
> **iv** The equal sides are also parallel.
>
> **v** The opposite angles are equal.
>
> **vi** All the four sides are equal.
>
> **vii** There are no right angles in the shape.

What is the shape?

Let's Explore!

16 A shape ABC has 3 sides. What is the shape?
If AC = BC, describe the shape.
Give another condition to make the shape ABC a right-angled isosceles triangle.

17 A shape ABCD has 4 sides. AB // CD and AD // BC. What is the shape?
If AB = BC, describe the shape.
Give another condition to make the shape ABCD a square.

Maths Journal

18 JKLM is a parallelogram. JK = KL and ∠JKL = 90°. Explain why JKLM is a square.

19

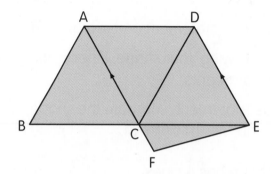

The shape above is not drawn to scale. ABCD is a rhombus and CFED is a trapezium in which DE // AF. BE and AF are straight lines.
Using '+', '=', '180°' or '360°', state the relationship between the angles in each set.

For example, in **a**, ∠ABC = ∠ADC.

a   ∠ABC and ∠ADC

b   ∠ACB and ∠ECF

c   ∠AFE and ∠DEF

d   ∠ACB and ∠BCF

e   ∠CAD and ∠ACD

f   ∠ACB, ∠ACD and ∠DCE

g   ∠BCD, ∠DCF and ∠BCF

The diagrams shown are not drawn to scale.

20 BCD is a triangle. AC, BE and CF are straight lines. ∠ABD = 134° and ∠FDE = 85°. Find ∠DBC and ∠BCD.

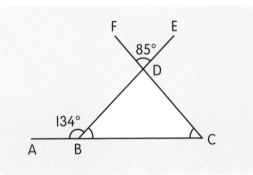

21 ABC is an isosceles triangle where AC = BC. ∠BEA = 78° and ∠CBE = 36°. Find ∠ABE.

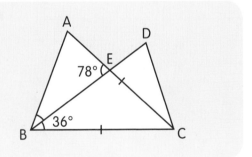

22 XYZ is an isosceles triangle where XY = XZ. ∠WXZ = 142° and ∠YXW = 106°. Find ∠YZX.

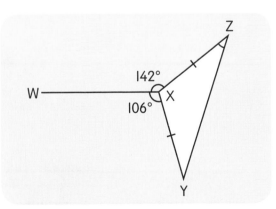

Let's Practise!

23 KLMN is a parallelogram. LK and JM are straight lines. ∠OLM = 68° and ∠KOM = 120°. Find ∠NJM.

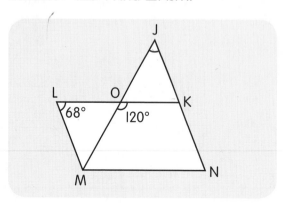

24 PQRS is a trapezium in which PS // QR. PQR is an equilateral triangle and ∠RSP = 35°. Find ∠PRS.

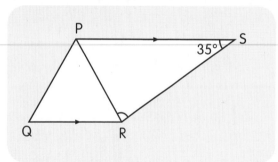

25 WXYZ is a rhombus and WSTZ is a parallelogram. ∠YZW = 54°. Find ∠ZYS and ∠TZY.

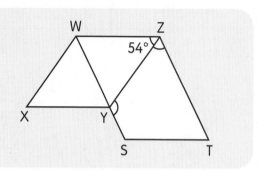

Practice Book 6A, p.27

Let's Wrap It Up!

You have learnt to find unknown angles in shapes and diagrams using the properties of:

- angles on a straight line
- angles at a point
- vertically opposite angles
- right-angled, isosceles, equilateral and other triangles
- square, rectangle, parallelogram, rhombus and trapezium.

Let's Revise!

The following shapes are not drawn to scale.

26 ABCD is a trapezium and DEF is a right-angled triangle. $\angle DEF = 90°$ and CB // DA. AE and CF are straight lines. Find $\angle EFD$.

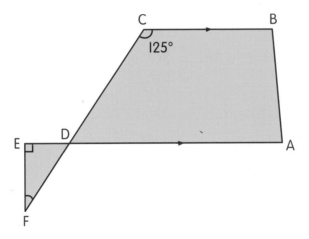

Since AD // BC, $\angle ADC = 180° - 125° = 55°$

$\angle EDF = \angle ADC = 55°$

$\angle EFD = 180° - 90° - 55° = 35°$

Let's Wrap It Up!

27 ABCD is a parallelogram and BECD is a rhombus. AE is a straight line. Find ∠CBE and ∠CDA.

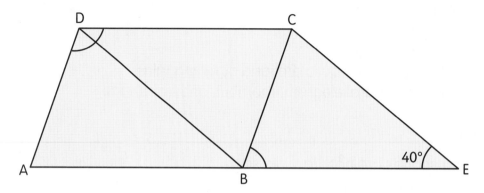

Since BECD is a rhombus, BE = CE.

∠CBE = (180° − 40°) ÷ 2
        = 70°

Since AE is a straight line, ∠ABC = 180° − 70°
        = 110°

Since ABCD is a parallelogram, ∠CDA = ∠ABC
        = 110°

Put On Your Thinking Caps!

28 ABCD is a square and ABE is an equilateral triangle. Find ∠CDE.

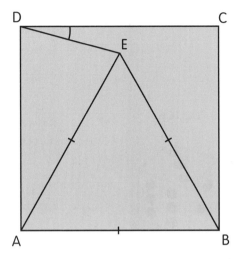

Practice Book 6A, p.36

Unit

3 Nets

Let's Learn!

 Solids

① The solid shown is a **cube**.

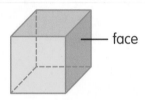 —— face

A cube has six faces.
The six faces are squares.

A dice is an example of a cube.

② The solids shown are **cuboids**.

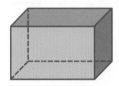

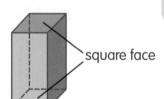 square face

A cuboid has six faces.
The six faces are rectangles.

Some cuboids have two faces that are squares.

Activity

③ Work in pairs.
You will need a cube and a cuboid.

a Count the number of faces on the cube. Then place the cube on a piece of paper and draw the outline of each face in turn.

b Write the names of the shapes of the faces you have drawn.

c Repeat **a** and **b** for the cuboid.

Activity

Then record your answers in a table as shown.

	Cube	Cuboid
Number of faces	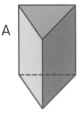	
Shape(s) of faces		

4 The solids shown are **prisms**.

A

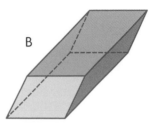

B

Prism A has five faces.
Three faces are rectangles
and two faces are triangles.

Prism B has six faces.
Four faces are rectangles and
two faces are parallelograms.

5 The solids shown are **pyramids**.

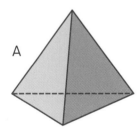
A

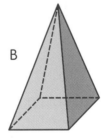
B

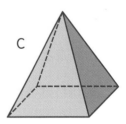
C

Pyramid A has four
faces. The four
faces are triangles.

Pyramid B has five faces.
Four faces are triangles
and one face is a square.

Pyramid C has five faces.
Four faces are triangles and
one face is a rectangle.

6 The solids shown are **cylinders**.

7 The solids shown are **cones**.

Activity

8 Work in pairs.
You will need the solids shown.

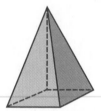

Solid A   Solid B   Solid C

a Count the number of faces on Solid A. Then place Solid A on a piece of paper and draw the outline of each face in turn.

b Write the names of the shapes of the faces you have drawn.

c Repeat **a** and **b** for every solid.

Then record your answers in a table as shown.

	Solid A	Solid B	Solid C
Number of faces			
Shape(s) of faces			

9 Name the shapes of these objects.

a

b

Tomato Soup

c

d

e

f

g

h

10 Work in groups of four.

a You will need a cube, a cuboid, a prism and a pyramid.

b Compare these pairs of solids:

i cube and cuboid   **ii** cube and prism

iii cube and pyramid   **iv** cuboid and prism

v cuboid and pyramid   **vi** prism and pyramid.

State the similarities and differences of each pair. Record your answers in a table.

Example

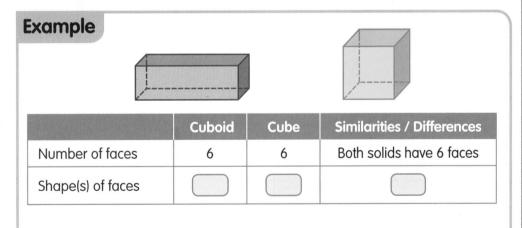

	Cuboid	Cube	Similarities / Differences
Number of faces	6	6	Both solids have 6 faces
Shape(s) of faces	⬭	⬭	⬭

Home Maths Encourage your child to identify different solids at home or in the supermarket. For example, ask your child to identify a cuboid object used as food packaging.

Let's Practise!

II For each solid shown below:

    a   name the solid

    b   state the number of faces it has

    c   state the shape(s) of its faces.

i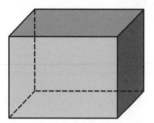

ii

iii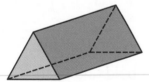

iv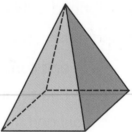

v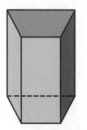

vi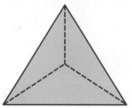

vii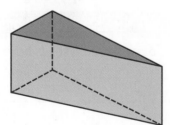

viii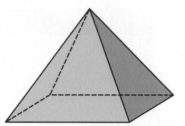

Practice Book 6A, p.39

Let's Learn!

 Nets of solids

1

The cube is cut along some of the edges and laid flat as shown below.

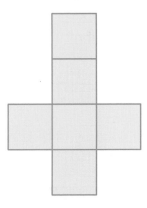

The diagram is called a **net** of the cube.

The net of a solid is a diagram that can be folded to make the solid.

2 Here are two other nets of the cube.

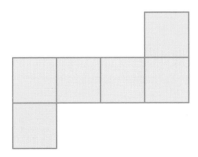 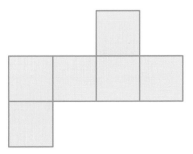

Trace them, cut them out and fold each net into a cube.

Activity

3 Trace and cut out these diagrams and try to fold each one into a cube.

a

b

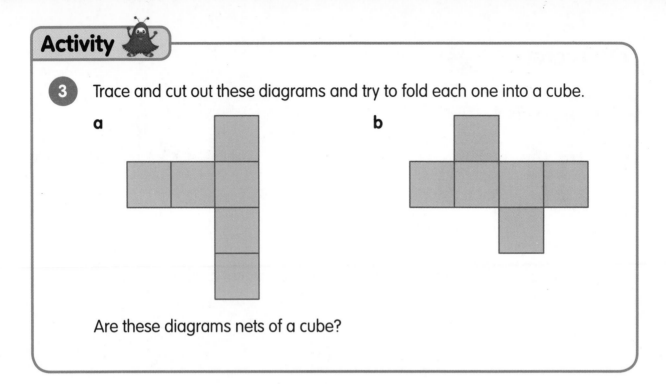

Are these diagrams nets of a cube?

4 Below are more examples of solids and their nets.

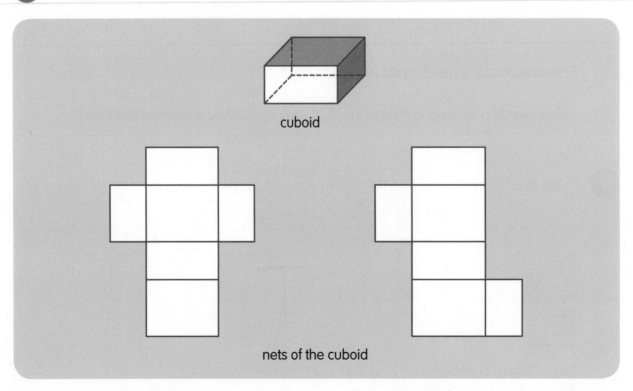

cuboid

nets of the cuboid

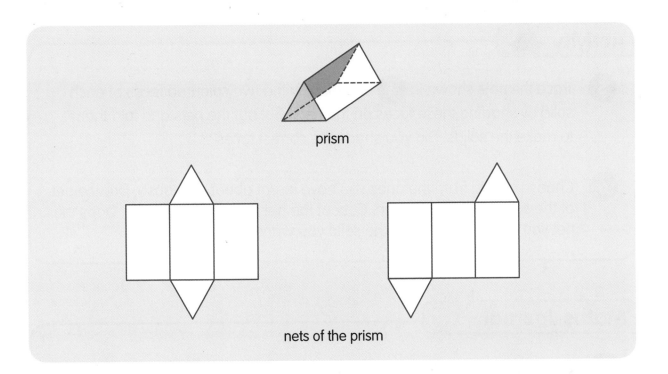

prism

nets of the prism

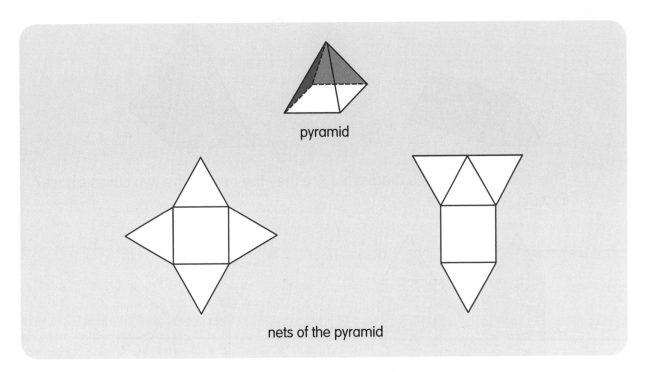

pyramid

nets of the pyramid

Home Maths

Give your child a cardboard box in the shape of a cube, cuboid, prism or pyramid. Help them to cut open the box to make a net of the solid.

Activity

5 Trace the nets shown in **4** and identify the two coloured faces of each solid by shading these faces on the nets. Cut out the nets and fold them to make the solids. Did you shade the correct faces?

6 Choose a solid from the ones you have learnt about previously. Draw a net of the solid you have chosen. Cut out the net and make the solid. Does the net you have drawn make the solid you wanted?

Maths Journal

7 Chantal was shown the two solids below.

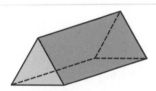 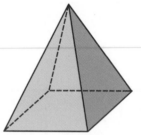

She drew the following diagrams. Are they the nets of the two solids above? Explain your answer.

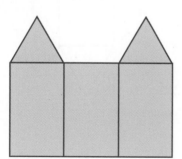 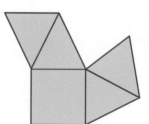

Let's Practise!

8 Below are the nets of four solids. Name the solid made by each net.

a

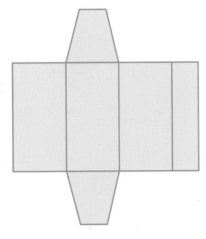

b

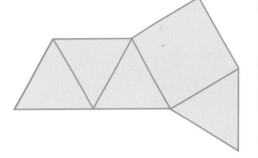

c

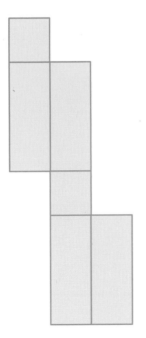

d

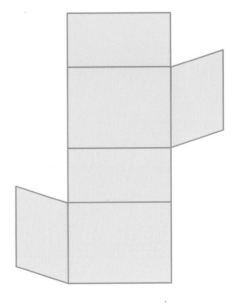

9 Match each solid to its net(s). There may be more than one net for each solid.

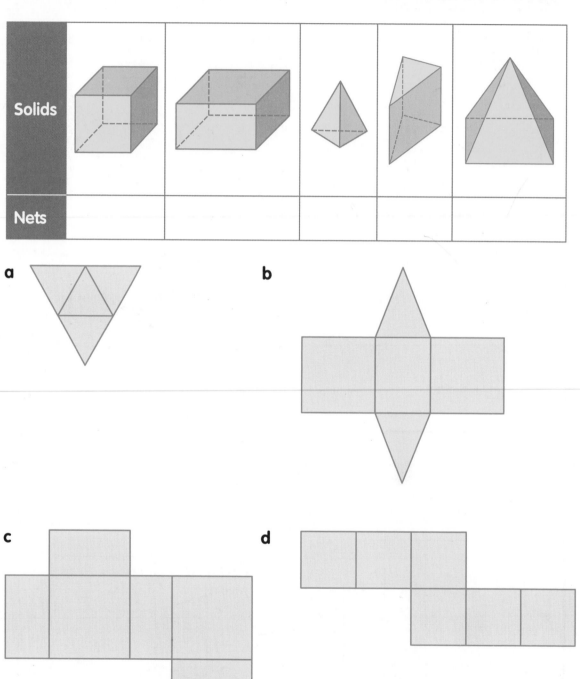

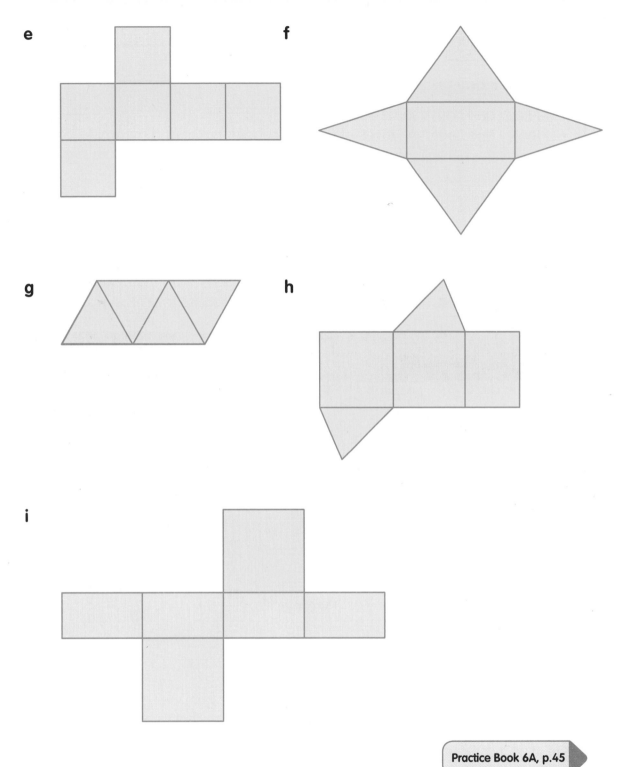

e

f

g

h

i

Practice Book 6A, p.45

Let's Wrap It Up!

You have learnt to:

- identify and name some solids
- identify and count the faces of a cube, cuboid, prism and pyramid
- identify the nets of a cube, cuboid, prism and pyramid
- identify the solid which is made from a net.

Let's Revise!

10 The table below shows four solids. Copy the table and complete the first three empty columns. From the diagrams shown on the next page, identify the net of each solid and write its letter in the last column.

Solids	Name of Solid	Number of Faces	Shape(s) of Faces	Nets
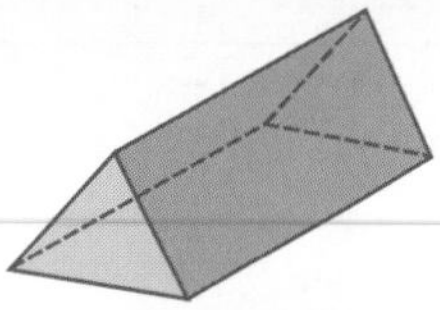	Prism	5	Triangle, Rectangle	f
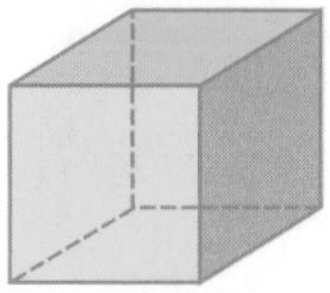	Cube	6	Square	a
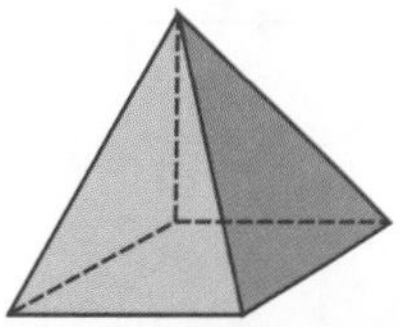	Pyramid	5	Square, Triangle	c
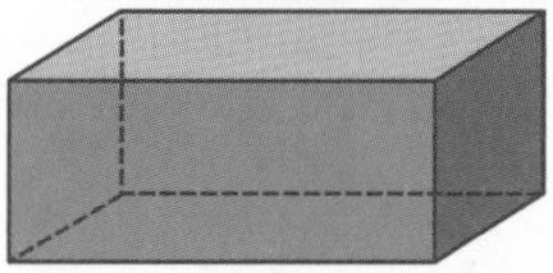	Cuboid	6	Square, Rectangle	d

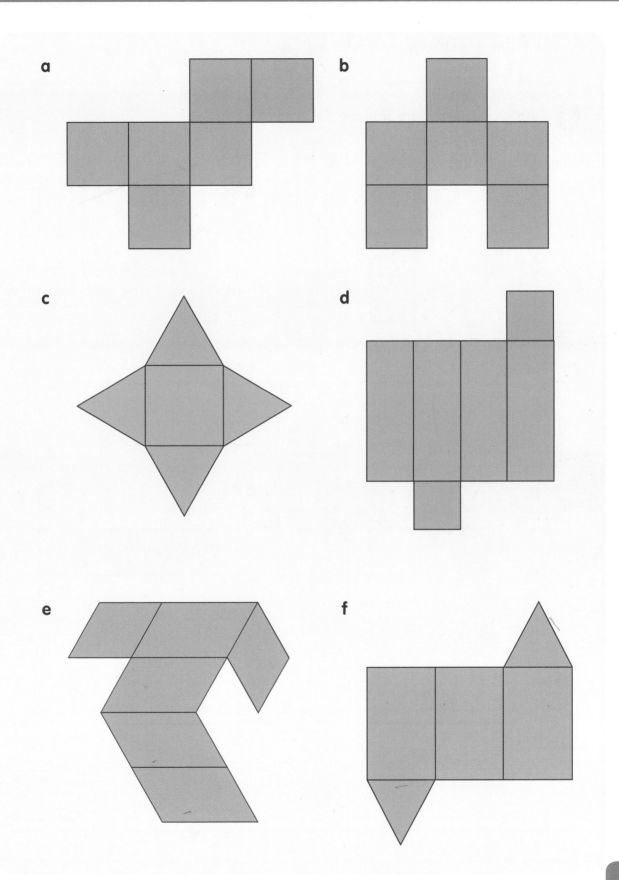

a

b

c

d

e

f

Put On Your Thinking Caps!

11 Which of these diagrams are the nets of a cube?

a

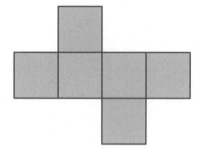

b

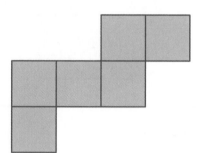

c

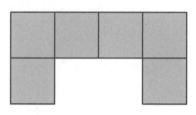

d

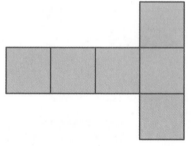

Put On Your Thinking Caps!

e

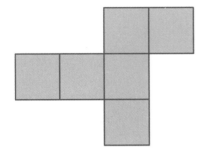

f

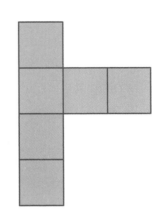

g

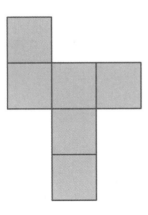

h

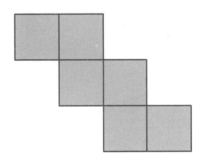

Practice Book 6A, p.55

4 Fractions

Let's Learn!

Four operations with fractions

1 Recall that:

a **i** $\dfrac{1}{4} + \dfrac{1}{8} = \dfrac{\boxed{}}{8} + \dfrac{\boxed{}}{8}$

$= \dfrac{\boxed{}}{8}$

ii $\dfrac{2}{3} + \dfrac{1}{2} = \dfrac{\boxed{}}{\boxed{}} + \dfrac{\boxed{}}{\boxed{}}$

$= \dfrac{\boxed{}}{\boxed{}}$

$= \boxed{}\dfrac{\boxed{}}{\boxed{}}$

b **i** $\dfrac{5}{6} - \dfrac{1}{12} = \dfrac{\boxed{}}{12} - \dfrac{\boxed{}}{12}$

$= \dfrac{\boxed{}}{12}$

$= \dfrac{\boxed{}}{\boxed{}}$

ii $\dfrac{4}{7} - \dfrac{1}{3} = \dfrac{\boxed{}}{\boxed{}} - \dfrac{\boxed{}}{\boxed{}}$

$= \dfrac{\boxed{}}{\boxed{}}$

c $\dfrac{2}{5} \times \dfrac{3}{4} = \dfrac{\boxed{} \times \boxed{}}{\boxed{} \times \boxed{}}$

$= \dfrac{\boxed{}}{\boxed{}}$

$= \dfrac{\boxed{}}{\boxed{}}$

I can also do this:

$\dfrac{2}{5} \times \dfrac{3}{4} = \dfrac{\overset{1}{2}}{5} \times \dfrac{3}{\underset{2}{4}}$

$= \dfrac{\boxed{}}{\boxed{}}$

d $\quad \dfrac{13}{4} \times \dfrac{4}{5} = \boxed{}\dfrac{\boxed{}}{\boxed{}}$

e $\quad \dfrac{6}{7} \div 3 = \dfrac{6^2}{7} \times \dfrac{1}{\cancel{3}_1}$

$\qquad\qquad = \dfrac{\boxed{}}{\boxed{}}$

f 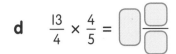 A gardener bought $2\dfrac{3}{4}$ kg of compost on Monday and another $4\dfrac{1}{6}$ kg on Tuesday. She filled 5 flower pots with $1\dfrac{1}{4}$ kg of compost each. How much compost did she have left?

$2\dfrac{3}{4} + 4\dfrac{1}{6} = \boxed{}\dfrac{\boxed{}}{\boxed{}}$

She bought $\boxed{}\dfrac{\boxed{}}{\boxed{}}$ kg of compost.

$1\dfrac{1}{4} \times 5 = \boxed{}\dfrac{\boxed{}}{\boxed{}}$

She used $\boxed{}\dfrac{\boxed{}}{\boxed{}}$ kg of compost.

$\boxed{}\dfrac{\boxed{}}{\boxed{}} - \boxed{}\dfrac{\boxed{}}{\boxed{}} = \dfrac{\boxed{}}{\boxed{}}$

She had $\dfrac{\boxed{}}{\boxed{}}$ kg of compost left.

Practice Book 6A, p.75

Let's Learn!

| Dividing by a proper fraction |

Dividing a whole number by a proper fraction

1 Farha cut a rectangular paper strip into a number of pieces. Each piece was $\frac{1}{2}$ of the paper strip. How many pieces did Farha cut the paper strip into?

Number of pieces = $1 \div \frac{1}{2}$

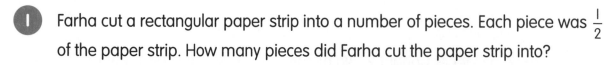

$1 \div \frac{1}{2}$ means this: "How many halves are there in 1 whole?"

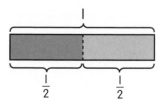

$\frac{1}{2}$ $\frac{1}{2}$

The model above shows that there are 2 halves in 1 whole.

So $1 \div \frac{1}{2} = 2$

Farha cut the rectangular paper strip into 2 pieces.

Activity

2 Work in pairs.
You will need 4 rectangular strips of paper. Each strip represents 1 whole.

a Use each strip to find:

i $1 \div \frac{1}{3}$ **ii** $1 \div \frac{1}{4}$

iii $1 \div \frac{1}{5}$ **iv** $1 \div \frac{1}{6}$

How many one-thirds, quarters, one-fifths and one-sixths are there in 1 whole?

Activity

b How many one-tenths are there in I whole?

$$1 \div \frac{\square}{\square} = \square$$

c How many one-twelfths are there in I whole?

$$1 \div \frac{\square}{\square} = \square$$

3 Lee cut 2 oranges into a number of pieces. Each piece was $\frac{1}{4}$ of an orange. How many pieces did Lee cut the 2 oranges into?

Number of pieces = $2 \div \frac{1}{4}$

$2 \div \frac{1}{4}$ means this: "How many quarters are there in 2 wholes?"

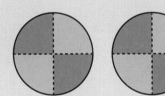

The model above shows that:

Number of quarters in I orange = 4

Number of quarters in 2 oranges = 2 × 4

So $2 \div \frac{1}{4}$ = 2 × 4

= 8

Dividing by $\frac{1}{4}$ is the same as multiplying by 4.

Lee cut the 2 oranges into 8 pieces.

4 Sarah cut 3 square pieces of paper into a number of pieces. Each piece was $\frac{1}{6}$ of a square piece of paper. How many pieces did Sarah cut the 3 square pieces of paper into?

Number of pieces = ☐ ÷ $\frac{☐}{☐}$

$3 \div \frac{1}{6}$ means this:

"How many one-sixths are there in 3 wholes?"

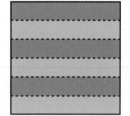 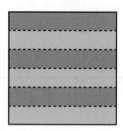 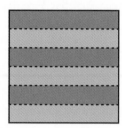

The model above shows that:

Number of one-sixths in 1 square piece of paper = ☐

Number of one-sixths in 3 square pieces of paper = ☐ × ☐

So $3 \div \frac{1}{6}$ = ☐ × ☐

= ☐

Dividing by $\frac{1}{6}$ is the same as multiplying by ☐.

Sarah cut the 3 square pieces of paper into ☐ pieces.

5 Find by multiplication.

a $3 \div \frac{1}{5}$ = ☐ × ☐ = ☐   **b** $7 \div \frac{1}{4}$ = ☐ × ☐ = ☐

c $4 \div \frac{1}{2}$ = ☐   **d** $5 \div \frac{1}{3}$ = ☐

e $6 \div \frac{1}{5}$ = ☐   **f** $8 \div \frac{1}{8}$ = ☐

Activity

6 Work in pairs.
You will need 5 identical rectangular strips of paper. Each strip represents
I whole.

a Take 2 strips of paper. Divide each of them into one-thirds and place
them as shown.
Then find $2 \div \frac{2}{3}$.

How many two-thirds are there in the 2 strips of paper?

There are ⬜ two-thirds in the 2 strips of paper.

So $2 \div \frac{2}{3} = $ ⬜

b Divide each of the other 3 strips of paper into quarters and place
them as shown.
Then find $3 \div \frac{3}{4}$.

How many three-quarters are there in the 3 strips of paper?

There are ⬜ three-quarters in the 3 strips of paper.

So $3 \div \frac{3}{4} = $ ⬜

7 What is $5 \div \frac{2}{3}$?

$$\frac{2}{3} \quad \frac{2}{3} \quad \frac{2}{3} \quad \frac{2}{3} \quad \frac{2}{3} \quad \frac{2}{3} \quad \frac{2}{3} \quad \frac{1}{2} \text{ of } \frac{2}{3}$$

How many $\frac{2}{3}$ are there in 5 wholes?

Number of two-thirds in 2 wholes = 3

Number of two-thirds in 1 whole = $\frac{3}{2}$

Number of two-thirds in 5 wholes = $5 \times \frac{3}{2}$

So $5 \div \frac{2}{3} = 5 \times \frac{3}{2}$

$$= \frac{15}{2} = 7\frac{1}{2}$$

Dividing by $\frac{2}{3}$ is the same as multiplying by $\frac{\square}{\square}$.

8 What is $7 \div \frac{3}{4}$?

$$\frac{3}{4} \quad \frac{3}{4} \quad \frac{3}{4} \quad \frac{3}{4} \quad \frac{3}{4} \quad \frac{3}{4} \quad \frac{3}{4} \quad \frac{3}{4} \quad \frac{3}{4} \quad \frac{1}{3} \text{ of } \frac{3}{4}$$

How many $\frac{3}{4}$ are there in 7 wholes?

Number of three-quarters in 3 wholes = 4

Number of three-quarters in 1 whole = $\frac{\square}{\square}$

Number of three-quarters in 7 wholes = $\square \times \frac{\square}{\square}$

So $7 \div \frac{3}{4} = \square \times \frac{\square}{\square}$

$$= \frac{\square}{\square}$$

$$= \square \frac{\square}{\square}$$

Dividing by $\frac{3}{4}$ is the same as multiplying by $\frac{\square}{\square}$.

Activity

9 A length of string is 3 m long.

Copy the model and divide each metre of string into one-thirds.

How many $\frac{2}{3}$m long pieces can the string be cut into? ⬭

What is the length of the remaining string? $\dfrac{\square}{\square}$ m

Now find the answer by division. Express your answer as a mixed number.

Number of pieces = $3 \div \dfrac{\square}{\square}$

$= 3 \times \dfrac{\square}{\square}$

$= \dfrac{\square}{\square}$

$= \square\dfrac{\square}{\square}$

The answer $4\frac{1}{2}$ means there are 4 pieces of string, each of length $\frac{2}{3}$m, and a remaining piece of string that is half of $\frac{2}{3}$m.

How many $\frac{2}{3}$m long pieces can the string be cut into? ⬭

What fraction of one piece of $\frac{2}{3}$m is the remaining string? $\dfrac{\square}{\square}$

What will be the length of the remaining string? $\dfrac{\square}{\square} \times \dfrac{\square}{\square} = \dfrac{\square}{\square}$ m

I can also find the remainder like this:

Total length of the 4 pieces of string $= 4 \times \dfrac{2}{3}$

$= 2\dfrac{2}{3}$m

Length of the remaining string $= 3 - 2\dfrac{2}{3}$

$= \dfrac{1}{3}$m

10 Find the value of each of the following.

a $\quad 4 \div \dfrac{4}{7}$

b $\quad 6 \div \dfrac{2}{7}$

c $\quad 9 \div \dfrac{3}{8}$

d $\quad 5 \div \dfrac{10}{13}$

e $\quad 10 \div \dfrac{5}{14}$

f $\quad 12 \div \dfrac{9}{10}$

Dividing a proper fraction by a proper fraction

 Activity

11 Work in pairs.
You will need 2 identical rectangular strips of paper.
Each strip represents 1 whole.

a Take one strip of paper and divide it into halves.
Then find $\dfrac{1}{2} \div \dfrac{1}{4}$.

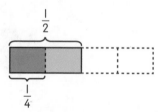

How many quarters are there in half?

So $\dfrac{1}{2} \div \dfrac{1}{4} = \boxed{}$

How can you also find $\dfrac{1}{2} \div \dfrac{1}{4}$ by multiplication?

What have you learnt about dividing by $\dfrac{1}{4}$?

$\dfrac{1}{2} \div \dfrac{1}{4} = \dfrac{\boxed{}}{\boxed{}} \times \boxed{}$

$= \boxed{}$

Activity

b   Divide the other strip of paper into one-thirds.

Then find $\frac{2}{3} \div \frac{1}{6}$.

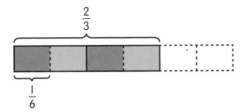

How many one-sixths are there in two-thirds?

So $\frac{2}{3} \div \frac{1}{6} = \boxed{}$

How can you also find $\frac{2}{3} \div \frac{1}{6}$ by multiplication?

What have you learnt about dividing by $\frac{1}{6}$?

$\frac{2}{3} \div \frac{1}{6} = \dfrac{\boxed{}}{\boxed{}} \times \boxed{}$

$\phantom{\frac{2}{3} \div \frac{1}{6}} = \boxed{}$

12 Ruby was given $\frac{3}{4}$ of a pizza. She cut it into a number of pieces. Each piece was $\frac{3}{8}$ of the pizza. How many pieces did Ruby cut it into?

Number of pieces = $\frac{3}{4} \div \frac{3}{8}$

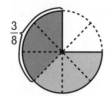

The model above shows that there are 2 three-eighths in $\frac{3}{4}$.

So $\frac{3}{4} \div \frac{3}{8} = 2$

We can now divide like this:

$\frac{3}{4} \div \frac{3}{8} = \frac{3}{4} \times \frac{8}{3}$

$\qquad = 2$

Ruby cut the pizza into 2 pieces.

Dividing by $\frac{3}{8}$ is the same as multiplying by $\dfrac{\square}{\square}$.

13 Hardeep had $\frac{5}{7}\ell$ of water. He poured the water into some cups. The capacity of each cup was $\frac{2}{7}\ell$. How many cups of water did Hardeep have?

Number of cups = $\dfrac{\square}{\square} \div \dfrac{\square}{\square}$

$\qquad = \dfrac{\square}{\square} \times \dfrac{\square}{\square}$

$\qquad = \dfrac{\square}{\square}$

$\qquad = \square\dfrac{\square}{\square}$

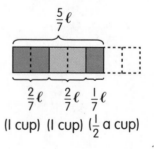

$\frac{5}{7}\ell$

$\frac{2}{7}\ell \quad \frac{2}{7}\ell \quad \frac{1}{7}\ell$

(1 cup) (1 cup) ($\frac{1}{2}$ a cup)

Hardeep had $\square\dfrac{\square}{\square}$ cups of water.

Activity

14 A jug contains $\frac{4}{5}\ell$ of orange juice.

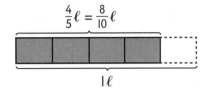

$\frac{4}{5}\ell = \frac{8}{10}\ell$

1ℓ

Copy the model above and divide it into one-tenths.

How many glasses, each containing $\frac{3}{10}\ell$, can the orange juice
be poured into? [　　]

How many litres of orange juice will be left? $\frac{\boxed{}}{\boxed{}}\ell$

Now find the answer by division. Express your answer as a mixed number.

Number of glasses $= \frac{4}{5} \div \dfrac{\boxed{}}{\boxed{}}$

$= \dfrac{4}{5} \times \dfrac{\boxed{}}{\boxed{}}$

$= \dfrac{\boxed{}}{\boxed{}}$

$= \boxed{}\dfrac{\boxed{}}{\boxed{}}$

> The answer $2\frac{2}{3}$ means there
> are 2 glasses of orange juice,
> each containing $\frac{3}{10}\ell$, and a
> remaining glass of orange
> juice that contains $\frac{2}{3}$ of $\frac{3}{10}\ell$.

How many glasses, each containing $\frac{3}{10}\ell$, can the orange juice
be poured into? [　　]

What fraction of one glass of $\frac{3}{10}\ell$ is the orange juice left? $\dfrac{\boxed{}}{\boxed{}}$

How many litres of orange juice will be left? $\dfrac{\boxed{}}{\boxed{}} \times \dfrac{\boxed{}}{\boxed{}} = \dfrac{\boxed{}}{\boxed{}}\ell$

I can also find the remainder like this:

Total amount of orange juice in 2 glasses $= 2 \times \dfrac{3}{10}$

$= \dfrac{3}{5}\ell$

Amount of orange juice left $= \dfrac{4}{5} - \dfrac{3}{5}$

$= \dfrac{1}{5}\ell$

15 Find the value of:

a $\dfrac{2}{3} \div \dfrac{1}{9}$

b $\dfrac{3}{5} \div \dfrac{1}{10}$

c $\dfrac{3}{4} \div \dfrac{1}{2}$

d $\dfrac{1}{6} \div \dfrac{2}{3}$

e $\dfrac{5}{8} \div \dfrac{15}{16}$

f $\dfrac{7}{16} \div \dfrac{5}{12}$

16 A bottle contains $2\,\ell$ of sunflower oil. A cook uses $\dfrac{1}{12}\ell$ of sunflower oil per day. How many days will the bottle of sunflower oil last?

2ℓ

| $\frac{1}{12}\ell$ | $\frac{1}{12}\ell$ | | $\frac{1}{12}\ell$ | $\frac{1}{12}\ell$ |

? days

Number of days $= 2 \div \dfrac{1}{12} = 2 \times 12$

$= 24$

The bottle of sunflower oil will last 24 days.

17 A chef buys $12\,\text{kg}$ of spaghetti each day. He uses $\dfrac{2}{11}\,\text{kg}$ of spaghetti for each pot of spaghetti he cooks. When he has used up all the spaghetti, how many pots of spaghetti would he have cooked?

$12\,\text{kg}$

| $\frac{2}{11}$ kg | $\frac{2}{11}$ kg | | $\frac{2}{11}$ kg | $\frac{2}{11}$ kg |

? pots

Number of pots $= \boxed{} \div \dfrac{\boxed{}}{\boxed{}}$

$= \boxed{} \times \dfrac{\boxed{}}{\boxed{}}$

$= \boxed{}$

He would have cooked $\boxed{}$ pots of spaghetti.

18 A plank is $\frac{4}{5}$ m in length. A worker cuts it into some pieces and each piece is $\frac{1}{10}$ m long. How many pieces did he cut the plank into?

$\frac{4}{5}$ m

| $\frac{1}{10}$ m | $\frac{1}{10}$ m | | $\frac{1}{10}$ m | $\frac{1}{10}$ m |

Number of pieces = $\frac{4}{5} \div \frac{1}{10}$

$= \frac{4}{5} \times 10$

$= 8$

He cut the plank into 8 pieces.

19 Lizzy had $\frac{2}{3}$ of a pizza. She cut it into a number of pieces. Each piece was $\frac{1}{9}$ of the whole pizza. How many pieces did she cut it into?

$\frac{2}{3}$ of a pizza

| $\frac{1}{9}$ | $\frac{1}{9}$ | | $\frac{1}{9}$ | $\frac{1}{9}$ |

Number of pieces = $\dfrac{\square}{\square} \div \dfrac{\square}{\square}$

$= \dfrac{\square}{\square} \times \square$

$= \square$

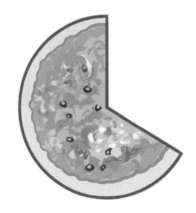

She cut it into $\square$ pieces.

Let's Explore!

20 Work out the following:

  a $4 \div \frac{2}{5}$ and $\frac{2}{5} \div 4$

  b $\frac{1}{4} \div \frac{2}{3}$ and $\frac{2}{3} \div \frac{1}{4}$

  c $\frac{4}{5} \div \frac{3}{10}$ and $\frac{3}{10} \div \frac{4}{5}$

  d $\frac{5}{8} \div \frac{3}{4}$ and $\frac{3}{4} \div \frac{5}{8}$

  What do you notice about the answers to each pair of divisions?

  Given that $\frac{6}{7} \div 9 = \frac{2}{21}$ and $\frac{10}{11} \div \frac{5}{6} = \frac{12}{11}$, find without further workings:

  i $9 \div \frac{6}{7}$

  ii $\frac{5}{6} \div \frac{10}{11}$

Maths Journal

21 Explain in words, the meaning of:

  a $5 \div \frac{2}{5}$

  b $\frac{4}{7} \div \frac{1}{2}$

22 Zahra and Ben worked out $\frac{3}{4} \div \frac{1}{8}$ like this:

Zahra	Ben
$\frac{3}{4} \div \frac{1}{8} = \frac{4}{3} \times \frac{1}{8}$	$\frac{3}{4} \div \frac{1}{8} = \frac{4}{3} \times 8$
$= \frac{4}{24}$	$= \frac{32}{3}$
$= \frac{1}{6}$	$= 10\frac{2}{3}$

  Explain what they did incorrectly. What should the answer be?

Let's Practise!

23 Use the models to find the answers.

a $1 \div \frac{1}{4}$

b $3 \div \frac{3}{5}$

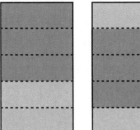 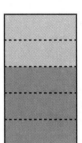

c $\frac{3}{4} \div \frac{1}{8}$

d $\frac{2}{3} \div \frac{2}{9}$

24 Find by multiplication.

a $4 \div \frac{1}{7}$

b $12 \div \frac{1}{3}$

c $9 \div \frac{3}{4}$

d $10 \div \frac{4}{5}$

e $\frac{1}{2} \div \frac{1}{8}$

f $\frac{1}{4} \div \frac{1}{2}$

g $\frac{3}{5} \div \frac{11}{15}$

h $\frac{2}{3} \div \frac{10}{13}$

Let's Practise!

Solve these word problems. Show your workings clearly.

25 4 melons were shared among a group of children. Each child got $\frac{2}{9}$ of a melon. How many children were there in the group?

26 A rectangle has an area of 9 m². It is cut up into a number of parts. Each part has an area of $\frac{3}{8}$ m². How many parts has the rectangle been cut into?

27 $\frac{5}{6}$ of a pie was left. Kate cut it into a number of pieces. Each piece was $\frac{1}{18}$ of the whole pie. How many pieces did Kate cut it into?

28 The tins of food in a pack have a total mass of $\frac{15}{16}$ kg. Each tin of food has a mass of $\frac{5}{32}$ kg. How many tins of food are there in the pack?

29 A plank 4 m long is cut into a number of pieces. Each piece is $\frac{3}{5}$ m long.

   a How many pieces of length $\frac{3}{5}$ m has the plank been cut into?

   b What is the length of the remaining plank?

30 A baker has $\frac{5}{6}$ kg of flour. She uses it to bake loaves of bread. Each loaf contains $\frac{2}{9}$ kg of flour.

   a How many loaves has she baked?

   b What is the mass of the remaining flour?

31 A roll of ribbon was 8 m long. Joe cut 6 pieces of ribbon, each of length $\frac{2}{3}$ m, to tie some presents. He then cut the remaining ribbon into some pieces, each of length $\frac{3}{4}$ m.

   a How many pieces of ribbon, each $\frac{3}{4}$ m in length, did Joe have?

   b What was the length of ribbon left over?

Practice Book 6A, p.77

Let's Learn!

Word problems

1. Mr Taylor drives from his house to his office and passes a library on the way. His house is $4\frac{1}{2}$ km away from the library. The distance between the library and his office is $2\frac{3}{8}$ km shorter than the distance between the library and his house. What is the distance between his house and his office?

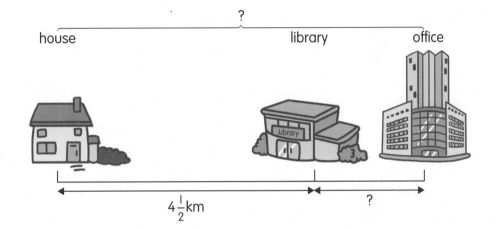

$$\boxed{}\frac{\boxed{}}{\boxed{}} - \boxed{}\frac{\boxed{}}{\boxed{}} = \boxed{}\frac{\boxed{}}{\boxed{}}$$

The distance between the library and his office is $\boxed{}\frac{\boxed{}}{\boxed{}}$ km.

$$\boxed{}\frac{\boxed{}}{\boxed{}} + \boxed{}\frac{\boxed{}}{\boxed{}} = \boxed{}\frac{\boxed{}}{\boxed{}}$$

The distance between his house and his office is $\boxed{}\frac{\boxed{}}{\boxed{}}$ km.

2 A school raises some money at a concert. The children chose to spend $\frac{1}{3}$ of the money on a trip, give $\frac{3}{8}$ of the reminder to the school fund and share the rest equally between 3 charities.

a What fraction of the money does each charity receive?

b If the concert raises £5400, how much does each charity get?

a **Method I**

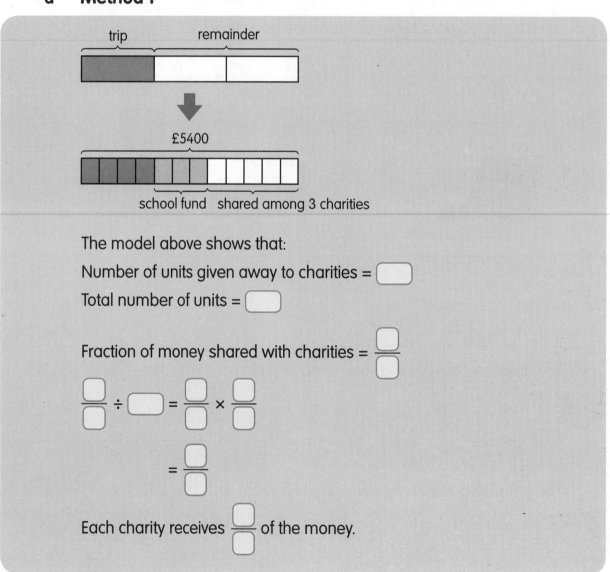

The model above shows that:

Number of units given away to charities = ◻

Total number of units = ◻

Fraction of money shared with charities = ◻/◻

◻/◻ ÷ ◻ = ◻/◻ × ◻/◻

= ◻/◻

Each charity receives ◻/◻ of the money.

Method 2

$$1 - \frac{1}{3} = \frac{\square}{\square} \text{ (remainder)}$$

$$\frac{3}{8} \times \frac{\square}{\square} = \frac{\square}{\square} \text{ (school fund)}$$

$$\frac{\square}{\square} - \frac{\square}{\square} = \frac{\square}{\square} \text{ (shared among 3 charities)}$$

$$\frac{\square}{\square} \div \square = \frac{\square}{\square} \times \frac{\square}{\square}$$

$$= \frac{\square}{\square}$$

Each charity receives $\frac{\square}{\square}$ of the money.

b $\dfrac{\square}{\square} \times £5400 = £\boxed{}$

Each charity gets £$\boxed{}$.

3 Miss Green used $\frac{2}{3}$ of her garden to plant tomatoes and another $\frac{1}{9}$ of it to plant lettuce. She then divided the rest of her garden into several small flower beds. Each small flower bed was $\frac{1}{18}$ of her garden.

a How many small flower beds were there?

b If the area of her garden was 72 m², what was the area of each small flower bed?

a Fraction of land divided $= 1 - \frac{2}{3} - \frac{1}{9} = \frac{2}{9}$

$$\frac{2}{9} \div \frac{1}{18} = \frac{2}{9} \times 18$$
$$= 4$$

There were 4 small flower beds.

b $\frac{1}{18} \times 72 = 4$

Each small flower bed was 4 m².

4 $\frac{2}{3}$ of a square is coloured green. Sophie cuts this part into a number of pieces such that each piece is $\frac{1}{9}$ of the whole square.

a Find the number of pieces Sophie has.

b If the area of the square is 45 cm², what is the area of each piece?

a Number of pieces = $\frac{\square}{\square} \div \frac{\square}{\square}$

= $\frac{\square}{\square} \times \square$

= $\square$

Sophie has $\square$ pieces.

b Area of green part = $\frac{\square}{\square} \times 45 = 30$ cm²

$30 \div \square = \square$

The area of each piece is $\square$ cm².

5 $\frac{3}{5}$ of the pupils in a class were boys. The teacher divided the boys equally into groups such that each group of boys had $\frac{1}{10}$ of the number of pupils in the class. The teacher then divided the girls equally into groups such that each group of girls had $\frac{1}{5}$ of the number of pupils in the class.

a Find the number of groups of boys and the number of groups of girls.

b If there were 16 girls in the class, how many boys were there in each group?

a   Number of groups of boys = $\dfrac{\square}{\square} \div \dfrac{\square}{\square}$

$= \dfrac{\square}{\square} \times \square$

$= \square$

Number of groups of girls = $\dfrac{\square}{\square} \div \dfrac{\square}{\square}$

$= \dfrac{\square}{\square} \times \square$

$= \square$

There were $\square$ groups of boys and $\square$ groups of girls.

b $\dfrac{2}{5}$ of the class ⟶ 16 pupils

$\dfrac{1}{5}$ of the class ⟶ $\square$ pupils

$\dfrac{3}{5}$ of the class ⟶ $\square$ pupils

$\square \div 6 = \square$

There were $\square$ boys in each group.

Let's Practise!

Solve these word problems. Draw models to help you where necessary.

6   A length of pipe was $2\dfrac{1}{3}$ m long. Another length of pipe was $\dfrac{5}{6}$ m shorter. A plumber joined the two pipes together. What was the total length of the pipe in the end?

7   A farmer picked some apples. She sold $\dfrac{2}{3}$ of them and gave $\dfrac{1}{5}$ of the remainder to her friend. She had 40 apples left. How many apples did she pick?

Let's Practise!

8 Liam read the first $\frac{1}{6}$ of a book on Monday and another $\frac{1}{3}$ of it on Tuesday. He took another 4 days to finish reading the book. He read the same number of pages on each of these 4 days.

    a What fraction of the book did he read on each of these 4 days?

    b If he read 30 pages on each of these 4 days, find the number of pages in the book.

9 In June, Ella visited her aunt for a total of 8 hours. She spent $\frac{4}{5}$ hours at her aunt's house for each visit.

    a Find the number of visits she made in June.

    b In July, she spent twice the amount of time she spent in June. How many visits did she make in July?

10 A drama club spent $\frac{3}{10}$ of its budget on stage lights, $\frac{1}{5}$ of it on costumes and the rest on hiring a theatre. The theatre cost $\frac{1}{8}$ of the budget for each night of the show.

    a Find how many nights the show was performed.

    b If the budget was £2400, how much money did the theatre cost each night?

11 Josh used $\frac{3}{8}$ of his money to buy some tennis balls and $\frac{2}{5}$ of the remainder to buy 2 tennis rackets. A tennis racket costs 3 times as much as a tennis ball. How many tennis balls did he buy?

Practice Book 6A, p.85

Let's Wrap It Up!

You have learnt to:

- divide a whole number by a proper fraction
- divide a proper fraction by another proper fraction.

Let's Revise!

12 $12 \div \dfrac{3}{8} = 12 \times \dfrac{8}{3}$

$\qquad\qquad = 32$

13 $\dfrac{5}{6} \div \dfrac{10}{11} = \dfrac{5}{6} \times \dfrac{11}{10}$

$\qquad\qquad = \dfrac{11}{12}$

14   A square piece of cardboard has an area of $\dfrac{4}{9}$ m². Nick cut it into a number of pieces, each with an area of $\dfrac{2}{27}$ m². How many pieces did Nick cut the cardboard into?

Number of pieces $= \dfrac{4}{9} \div \dfrac{2}{27}$

$\qquad\qquad\qquad = \dfrac{4}{9} \times \dfrac{27}{2}$

$\qquad\qquad\qquad = 6$

Nick cut the cardboard into 6 pieces.

Put On Your Thinking Caps!

15 Mr Carson cooked a stew. He divided the stew equally into portions of $\frac{1}{5}$ kg each. If he divided it equally into portions of $\frac{1}{8}$ kg each, he will get 12 more portions of stew. How many kilograms of stew did he cook? (Assume that the mass of stew is a whole number.)

Practice Book 6A, p.93   Practice Book 6A, p.94

Let's Learn!

Ratio and fraction

1 Omar has 9 pencils. Millie has 15 pencils.

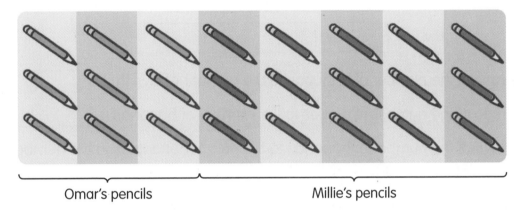

Omar's pencils   Millie's pencils

We can show the number of pencils both children have by using a model.

Omar's pencils   Millie's pencils

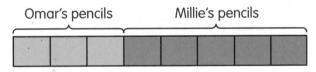

We can also arrange the model in another way.

Omar's pencils

Millie's pencils

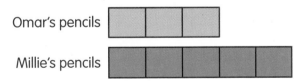

The ratio of the number of Omar's pencils to the number of Millie's pencils is 3 : 5.

The ratio of the number of Millie's pencils to the number of Omar's pencils is 5 : 3.

2 There are 4 bananas, 6 apples and 8 kiwi fruit in a basket.

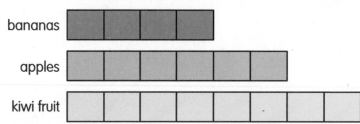

The ratio of the number of bananas to the number of kiwi fruit is ⬭ : ⬭ .

The ratio of the number of apples to the number of bananas is ⬭ : ⬭ .

The ratio of the number of bananas to the number of apples to the number of kiwi fruit is ⬭ : ⬭ : ⬭ .

The ratio of the number of kiwi fruit to the number of bananas to the number of apples is ⬭ : ⬭ : ⬭ .

3 The lengths of two sticks, A and B are represented using a model.

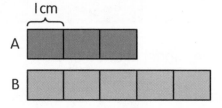

Total length of the two sticks = 3 + 5 = 8 cm

The ratio of the length of Stick A to the total length of the two sticks is 3 : 8.
So the length of Stick A is $\frac{3}{8}$ of the total length of the two sticks.

The ratio of the length of Stick A to the length of Stick B is 3 : 5. So the length of Stick A is $\frac{3}{5}$ of the length of Stick B.

The ratio of the length of Stick B to the length of Stick A is 5 : 3. So the length of Stick B is $\frac{5}{3}$ of the length of Stick A.

4   The masses of a rabbit, a chicken and a sheep are shown below.

I unit

rabbit

chicken

sheep

The ratio of the mass of the chicken to the mass of the sheep is ⬭ : ⬭ .

The mass of the chicken is $\dfrac{\square}{\square}$ of the mass of the sheep.

The mass of the sheep is $\dfrac{\square}{\square}$ of the mass of the chicken.

The ratio of the mass of the rabbit to the mass of the sheep is ⬭ : ⬭ .

The mass of the rabbit is $\dfrac{\square}{\square}$ of the mass of the sheep.

The mass of the sheep is $\dfrac{\square}{\square}$ of the mass of the rabbit.

The ratio of the mass of the rabbit to the total mass of the three animals is ⬭ : ⬭ .

The mass of the rabbit is $\dfrac{\square}{\square}$ of the total mass of the three animals.

5 The ratio of Sam's height to his little brother's height is 5 : 2.

    a The ratio of Sam's height to the total height of the two boys is ⬚ : ⬚ .

    b His brother's height is $\frac{\square}{\square}$ of Sam's height.

    c Sam's height is $\frac{\square}{\square}$ of his brother's height.

6 The number of adults and children watching a film is represented by this model.

adults ▧▧▧▧

children ▨▨▨▨▨▨▨▨▨▨▨▨

    a The ratio of the number of adults to the number of children is 4 : 12 = 1 : 3.

    b The ratio of the number of children to the number of adults is ⬚ : ⬚ .

    c The number of adults is $\frac{1}{3}$ of the number of children.

    d The number of children is $\frac{3}{1}$ of the number of adults.

       So the number of children is 3 times as many as the number of adults.

7 Miss Taylor spent £21 and Mr Jackson spent £42.

    a The ratio of the amount of money Miss Taylor spent to the amount of money Mr Jackson spent is ⬚ : ⬚ .

    b The amount of money Miss Taylor spent is $\frac{\square}{\square}$ of the amount of money Mr Jackson spent.

    c The amount of money Mr Jackson spent is ⬚ times the amount of money Miss Taylor spent.

8 Michael saved $\frac{3}{4}$ as much money as Poppy.

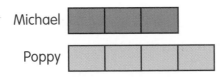

a The ratio of Michael's savings to Poppy's savings is 3 : 4.

b The ratio of Poppy's savings to their total savings is 4 : 7.

c Poppy's savings were $\frac{4}{7}$ of their total savings.

9 Peter cut a rope into two pieces. The length of the first piece was $\frac{4}{7}$ of the length of the second piece.

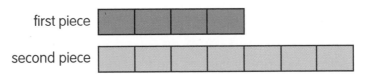

a The ratio of the length of the first piece to that of the second piece was

⬜ : ⬜ .

b The ratio of the length of the second piece to the total length was

⬜ : ⬜ .

c The length of the second piece was $\frac{\square}{\square}$ of the total length.

Let's Explore!

10 In the following table, you are given the ratio of a quantity to another quantity. Copy and complete the table.

Ratio Statement	Fraction Statement
A : B = 3 : 8	A is ▢/▢ of B
C : D = 4 : 7	C is ▢/▢ of D
E : F = 5 : 9	E is ▢/▢ of F

Compare the first quantity of each ratio statement with the numerator of the fraction statement. Then compare the second quantity of each ratio statement with the denominator of the fraction statement.

What do you notice after comparing? Do you observe a pattern? Write a statement about the pattern that you have observed.

Maths Journal

11 Work in pairs.

Write three fraction statements for each of the following.

a   The ratio of the number of apples to the number of oranges is 4 : 7.

> **Example**
>
> The number of apples is $\frac{4}{7}$ of the number of oranges.

b   Mrs Lee saved £450 per month while Mr Lee saved £150 per month.

Let's Practise!

12 X represents 2 units of stamps and Y represents 7 units of stamps.

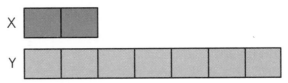

a   Find the ratio of X to Y.

b   X is $\dfrac{\square}{\square}$ of Y.   c   Y is $\dfrac{\square}{\square}$ of X.

13 The ratio of the length of Pole A to the length of Pole B is $4:5$.

a   Find the ratio of the length of Pole A to the total length of the two poles.

b   What fraction of the length of Pole A is the length of Pole B?

c   What fraction of the length of Pole B is the length of Pole A?

d   What fraction of the total length of the two poles is the length of Pole A?

e   What fraction of the total length of the two poles is the length of Pole B?

14 A cat's mass is $\dfrac{3}{5}$ of a dog's mass.

a   What is the ratio of the dog's mass to the cat's mass?

b   What is the ratio of the cat's mass to their total mass?

c   Express the cat's mass as a fraction of their total mass.

d   What fraction of the total mass is the dog's mass?

Let's Practise!

15 Jess had £15 and William had £21.

    a   Find the total amount of money they had altogether.

    b   Find the ratio of the amount of money Jess had to the amount of money that William had.

    c   Express the amount of money Jess had as a fraction of the amount of money that William had.

    d   Express the amount of money William had as a fraction of the amount of money that Jess had.

    e   Find the ratio of the amount of money Jess had to the total amount of money that they had altogether.

    f   Express the amount of money Jess had as a fraction of the total amount of money that they had altogether.

16 Three children, Anna, Bella and Cheng, share some beads in the ratio $2 : 3 : 4$.

    a   Express the number of beads Anna has as a fraction of the total number of beads.

    b   Express the number of beads Cheng has as a fraction of the number of beads Bella has.

    c   What fraction of the total number of beads Anna and Cheng have is the number of beads Bella has?

    d   How many times the number of beads Anna has is the number of beads Cheng has?

17 Steven bought a loaf of bread and cut it into three pieces. The mass of the first piece of bread was $\frac{5}{8}$ of the mass of the second piece of bread. The mass of the second piece of bread was $\frac{4}{7}$ of the mass of the third piece of bread.

    a   Find the ratio of the mass of the first piece of bread to that of the second piece of bread to that of the third piece of bread.

    b   What is the ratio of the mass of the second piece of bread to the total mass of the 3 pieces of bread?

    c   What fraction of the total mass of the 3 pieces of bread was the mass of the third piece of bread?

Practice Book 6A, p.95

Let's Learn!

Word problems (I)

1 Miss Green's salary is $\frac{5}{2}$ of Miss Brown's salary. Miss Green earns £895.

a Find the ratio of Miss Green's salary to Miss Brown's salary.

b How much do they earn altogether?

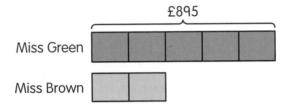

Total number of units = 5 + 2 = 7

The model above shows that:

a The ratio of Miss Green's salary to Miss Brown's salary is 5 : 2.

b 5 units ⟶ £895
I unit ⟶ £895 ÷ 5 = £179
7 units ⟶ £179 × 7 = £1253

They earn £1253 altogether.

2 The number of pupils School A has is $\frac{7}{3}$ of the number of pupils School B has. School A has 896 pupils.

a Find the ratio of the number of pupils School B has to the number of pupils School A has to the total number of pupils they have.

b How many pupils do they have altogether?

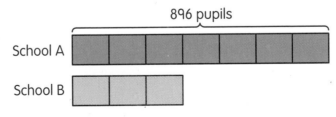

Total number of units = ⬚ + ⬚ = ⬚ units

The model on the previous page shows that:

a The ratio of the number of pupils School B has to the number of pupils School A has to the total number of pupils they have is ⬭ : ⬭ : ⬭.

b 7 units ⟶ ⬭ pupils

I unit ⟶ ⬭ ÷ ⬭ = ⬭ pupils

⬭ units ⟶ ⬭ × ⬭ = ⬭ pupils

They have ⬭ pupils altogether.

3 Mr Lee's savings are 4 times as much as Mr Clark's savings. Both people save a total of £120.

a What is the ratio of Mr Lee's savings to Mr Clark's savings to their total savings?

b What fraction of their total savings are Mr Lee's savings?

c What fraction of Mr Lee's savings are Mr Clark's savings?

d How much does Mr Lee save?

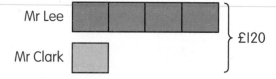

Mr Lee

Mr Clark

£120

a Total number of units = 5

The ratio of Mr Lee's savings to Mr Clark's savings to their total savings is 4 : 1 : 5.

b The ratio of Mr Lee's savings to their total savings is 4 : 5.

Mr Lee's savings are $\frac{4}{5}$ of the total savings.

c The ratio of Mr Clark's savings to Mr Lee's savings is 1 : 4.

Mr Clark's savings are $\frac{1}{4}$ of Mr Lee's savings.

d The model above shows that:

5 units ⟶ £120

I unit ⟶ £$\frac{120}{5}$ = £24

4 units ⟶ 4 × £24 = £96

Mr Lee saves £96.

The ratio of Mr Lee's savings to their total savings is 4 : 5.

Mr Lee's savings are $\frac{4}{5}$ of their total savings.

So Mr Lee's savings = $\frac{4}{5}$ × £120

= £96

4 Mr Green spent 5 times as much money as Miss Lim. Mr Green spent £13 448 more than Miss Lim.

a What is the ratio of the amount of money Mr Green spent to the amount of money Miss Lim spent to the total amount of money spent?

b What fraction of the total amount of money spent is the amount of money Mr Green spent?

c How much did each person spend?

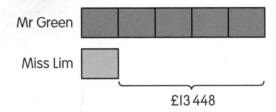

Mr Green

Miss Lim

£13 448

The model above shows that:

a The ratio of the amount of money Mr Green spent to the amount of money Miss Lim spent to the total amount of money spent is ( ) : ( ) : ( ).

b $\dfrac{\text{Amount Mr Green spent}}{\text{Total amount spent}} = \dfrac{\boxed{}}{\boxed{}}$

The amount of money Mr Green spent is $\dfrac{\boxed{}}{\boxed{}}$ of the total amount of money spent.

c ( ) units ⟶ £( )

( ) unit ⟶ £( )

( ) units ⟶ £( )

Mr Green spent £( ) and Miss Lim spent £( ).

5 The ratio of the number of football cards Meena has to the number of football cards George has is 3 : 2. The ratio of the number of football cards George has to the number of football cards Sarah has is 4 : 5. Meena, George and Sarah have 75 football cards altogether.

a Find the ratio of the number of football cards Meena has to the number of football cards Sarah has.

b How many football cards does Sarah have?

a

Meena's football cards : George's football cards

$$\times 2 \left(\begin{array}{c} 3:2 \\ 6:4 \end{array}\right) \times 2$$

Make George's ratio units the same for both.

George's football cards : Sarah's football cards
4 : 5

The ratio of the number of football cards Meena has to the number of football cards Sarah has is 6 : 5.

b **Method I**

Total number of units = 6 + 4 + 5 = 15

15 units ⟶ 75 football cards

1 unit ⟶ $\frac{75}{15}$ = 5 football cards

5 units ⟶ 5 × 5 = 25 football cards

Sarah has 25 football cards.

Method 2

The ratio of the number of football cards Sarah has to the total number of football cards is 5 : 15 = 1 : 3.

Sarah's football cards = $\frac{1}{3}$ × 75

= 25

Sarah has 25 football cards.

6 Anna, Ben and Jacob keep fish as pets. The ratio of the number of fish Anna has to the number of fish Ben has is 2 : 1. The ratio of the number of fish Ben has to the number of fish Jacob has is 2 : 3.

a Find the ratio of the number of fish Anna has to the number of fish Ben has to the number of fish Jacob has.

b If they have a total of 27 fish, how many fish do Anna and Ben have altogether?

a
Anna's fish : Ben's fish

× ▢ (2 : 1) × ▢
   ▢ : ▢

Ben's fish : Jacob's fish
2 : 3

The ratio of the number of fish Anna has to the number of fish Ben has to the number of fish Jacob has is ▢ : ▢ : ▢.

b **Method 1**

Total number of units = ▢

▢ units ⟶ ▢ fish

▢ unit ⟶ $\frac{▢}{▢}$ = ▢ fish

▢ units ⟶ ▢ × ▢ = ▢ fish

Anna and Ben have ▢ fish altogether.

Method 2

Anna's fish : Total number of fish = ▢ : ▢

Anna's fish = $\frac{▢}{▢}$ × ▢

= ▢

Ben's fish : Total number of fish = ▢ : ▢

Ben's fish = $\frac{▢}{▢}$ × ▢

= ▢

Anna and Ben have ▢ fish altogether.

7 The sides of a triangle are in the ratio 2 : 3 : 4. The sum of all the sides of the triangle is 162 cm. Find the length of the longest side of the triangle.

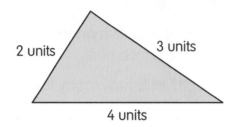

2 units

3 units

4 units

Sum of the three sides = 9 units

9 units ⟶ 162 cm

1 unit ⟶ 162 ÷ 9 = 18 cm

4 units ⟶ 4 × 18 = 72 cm

The length of the longest side of the triangle is 72 cm.

8 🖩 The sides of a right-angled triangle are in the ratio 5 : 12 : 13. The sum of the shortest side and the longest side is 144 cm. Find the length of the third side of the triangle.

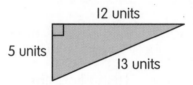

12 units

5 units

13 units

Sum of the shortest side and the longest side = 5 + 13

= ⬚ units

18 units ⟶ ⬚ cm

1 unit ⟶ $\dfrac{⬚}{⬚}$ = ⬚ cm

12 units ⟶ 12 × ⬚ = ⬚ cm

The length of the third side of the triangle is ⬚ cm.

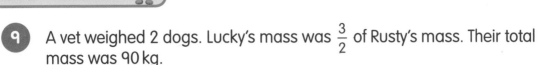

Let's Practise!

9 A vet weighed 2 dogs. Lucky's mass was $\frac{3}{2}$ of Rusty's mass. Their total mass was 90 kg.

a Find the ratio of Lucky's mass to Rusty's mass.

b What fraction of the total mass of the two dogs was Rusty's mass?

c What fraction of the total mass of the two dogs was Lucky's mass?

d Find the mass of each dog.

10 The mass of potatoes used by Mr Wood in his cooking was $\frac{5}{2}$ of the mass of carrots used. He used 9 kg more potatoes than carrots.

a Find the ratio of the mass of potatoes used to the mass of carrots used to the total mass of both ingredients.

b What fraction of the total mass of both ingredients was the mass of the potatoes?

c Find the total mass of both ingredients.

11 A wall has an area of 7·2 m². It was painted yellow and brown. The area of the wall painted yellow was 3 times as large as the area painted brown.

a What was the ratio of the area painted yellow to the area painted brown?

b What was the ratio of the area painted yellow to the area of the entire wall?

c What fraction of the area of the entire wall was painted brown?

d Find the area of the wall painted yellow.

Let's Practise!

12 Miss Taylor and Mr Green won some money on a game show. Miss Taylor won 5 times as much money as Mr Green. Mr Green won £4200 less than Miss Taylor.

a What was the ratio of the amount of money Miss Taylor won to the amount of money Mr Green won to the total amount of money both people won?

b What fraction of the total amount of money both people won did Miss Taylor win?

c What fraction of the total amount of money both people won did Mr Green win?

d How much money did each person win?

13 The ratio of the number of pupils in Group A to the number of pupils in Group B is 2 : 5. The ratio of the number of pupils in Group B to the number of pupils in Group C is 10 : 3.

a Find the ratio of the number of pupils in Group A to the number of pupils in Group B to the number of pupils in Group C.

b If there are 70 pupils in Group A and Group C altogether, how many pupils are there in Group B?

c However if Group B has 40 pupils, how many pupils are there in Group A and Group C altogether?

14 The ratio of the length of a rectangle to its width is 9 : 4. If the perimeter of the rectangle is 104 cm, find the area of the rectangle.

15 The ratio of the length of a parallelogram to that of its width is 7 : 4. The length is longer than the width by 746·1 cm. Find the perimeter of the parallelogram.

Practice Book 6A, p.103

Let's Learn!

Comparing ratios

1 Mr Smith made five mixtures of orange and pineapple juice using different amounts of juice. He recorded them in a table.

Mixture	A	B	C	D	E
Amount of orange juice (ml)	300	450	600	750	900
Amount of pineapple juice (ml)	200	300	400	500	600

Find the ratio of the amount of orange juice to the amount of pineapple juice in each mixture.

Mixture	A	B	C	D	E
Amount of orange juice : Amount of pineapple juice	3 : 2	3 : 2	3 : 2	3 : 2	3 : 2

What can you say about the ratios?
We say that the ratio of the amount of orange juice used to the amount of pineapple juice used is the **same** in each mixture.

We can also say that the amount of orange juice used and the amount of pineapple juice used are in a **fixed ratio**.

2 Mr Khan uses the following table to prepare four different mixtures of cement and sand. Complete the table.

Number of buckets of cement	4	8	12	16
Number of buckets of sand	3	6	9	12
Number of buckets of cement : number of buckets of sand	4 : 3	8 : 6	☐ : ☐	☐ : ☐
Number of buckets of cement : number of buckets of sand (simplest form)	4 : 3	4 : 3	☐ : ☐	☐ : ☐
Number of buckets of cement ⟋ Number of buckets of sand	$\frac{4}{3}$	$\frac{4}{3}$	$\frac{☐}{☐}$	$\frac{☐}{☐}$

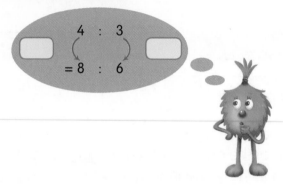

$$☐ \quad 4 : 3 \quad ☐$$
$$= 8 : 6$$

What can you say about the ratios in the fourth row of the table?

Are all the ratios the same? ☐

What can you say about the fractions in the fifth row of the table?

Are all the fractions the same? ☐

So the number of buckets of cement used and the number of buckets of sand used are in a fixed ratio.

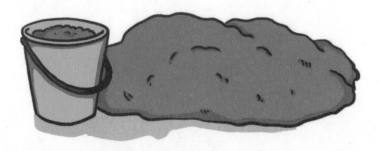

3 To make some dough, Amina mixes 5 cups of flour with every 3 cups of water.

a Find the ratio of the amount of flour used to the amount of water used.

b If Amina wants to make 5 times the amount of dough as above, how many cups of water and how many cups of flour does she need?

c If she uses 21 cups of water, how many cups of flour are needed to make the same type of dough?

a The ratio of the amount of flour used to the amount of water used is 5 : 3.

b

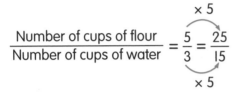

$$\frac{\text{Number of cups of flour}}{\text{Number of cups of water}} = \frac{5}{3} = \frac{25}{15}$$

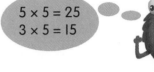

$5 \times 5 = 25$
$3 \times 5 = 15$

Amina needs 15 cups of water and 25 cups of flour.

c **Method 1**

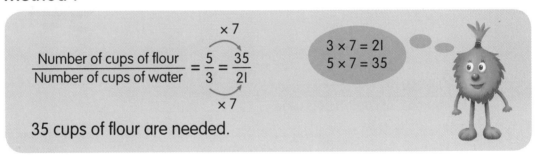

$$\frac{\text{Number of cups of flour}}{\text{Number of cups of water}} = \frac{5}{3} = \frac{35}{21}$$

$3 \times 7 = 21$
$5 \times 7 = 35$

35 cups of flour are needed.

Method 2

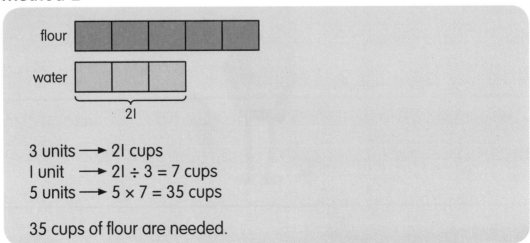

flour

water

21

3 units ⟶ 21 cups
1 unit ⟶ 21 ÷ 3 = 7 cups
5 units ⟶ 5 × 7 = 35 cups

35 cups of flour are needed.

97

4 Mr Lee prepares porridge for his family. For each bowl of porridge, he always uses 3 cups of water for every 2 cups of oats.

a Find the ratio of the number of cups of water used to the number of cups of oats used.

b If he wants to prepare 5 bowls of porridge, how many cups of water and how many cups of oats does he need?

c If he uses 18 cups of oats, how many cups of water does he need?

a The ratio of the number of cups of water used to the number of cups of oats used is ⬭ : ⬭.

b $\dfrac{\text{Number of cups of water used}}{\text{Number of cups of oats used}} = \dfrac{3}{2} = \dfrac{\square}{\square}$

Mr Lee needs ⬭ cups of water and ⬭ cups of oats.

$\times 5$

$\dfrac{3}{2} = \dfrac{15}{10}$

$\times 5$

c $\dfrac{\text{Number of cups of water used}}{\text{Number of cups of oats used}} = \dfrac{3}{2} = \dfrac{\square}{\square}$

Mr Lee needs ⬭ cups of water.

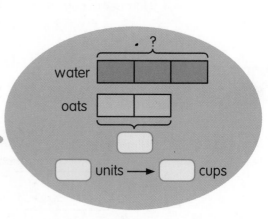

water

oats

?

⬭ units ⟶ ⬭ cups

5 Omar mixed 200 ml of squash with every 500 ml of water to make a drink for a party.

a Complete the table if the ratio of the amount of squash to the amount of water is the same.

Amount of squash (ml)	200	600	1000	⬚	1800
Amount of water (ml)	500	1500	⬚	3500	⬚
Amount of squash : amount of water			⬚ : ⬚		

b Based on the table in **a**, how much water is needed if 800 ml of squash is used?

c Based on the table in **a**, how much squash is needed if 400 ml of water is used?

b

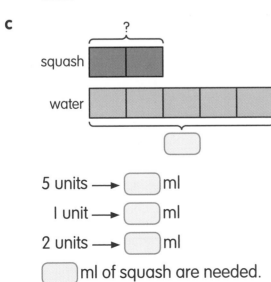

squash

water

?

2 units ⟶ ⬚ ml

1 unit ⟶ ⬚ ml

5 units ⟶ ⬚ ml

⬚ ml of water are needed.

c

?

squash

water

⬚

5 units ⟶ ⬚ ml

1 unit ⟶ ⬚ ml

2 units ⟶ ⬚ ml

⬚ ml of squash are needed.

Activity

6 Work in groups of four.

a You will need some green and red counters.

i Make different groups of counters so that the ratio of the number of green counters to the number of red counters in each group is 3 : 2. Record your results in a table.

Example

Group	A	B	C	D
Number of green counters	3	⬭	⬭	⬭
Number of red counters	2	⬭	⬭	⬭

ii If there are 72 red counters in a group, how many green counters are there?

b Each group will need a cup, a spoon, 4 empty jars, a jug of water and a bottle of food colouring.

i In a jar, mix 1 spoonful of food colouring with 3 cups of water.

ii Prepare 3 more jars of the same type of mixture as in **i** using different amounts of food colouring and water. Record the amounts of water and food colouring used in a table.

iii If 75 cups of water are used, how many spoonfuls of food colouring are needed?

Home Maths Look at some recipes with your child. Together, find the ratios between some of the ingredients.

Let's Practise!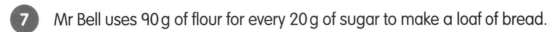

7 Mr Bell uses 90 g of flour for every 20 g of sugar to make a loaf of bread.

a Find the ratio of the mass of flour to the mass of sugar used.

b To make the loaf of bread, how many grams of sugar does Mr Bell need if he uses 270 g of flour?

c If he makes 5 loaves of the same type, how many grams of flour and how many grams of sugar will he use?

8 Beth uses 3 teaspoons of lemon juice for every 8 oranges to make a drink.

a Find the ratio of the number of oranges used to the number of teaspoons of lemon juice used.

b To make the same type of drink, how many teaspoons of lemon juice does Beth need if she uses 24 oranges?

c To make the same type of drink, how many oranges does Beth use if she uses 24 teaspoons of lemon juice?

9 In a science experiment, Mark mixed water and vinegar in the ratio 3 : 1.

a If he used 745·2 ml of water, how many millilitres of vinegar did he use?

b If 0·28 ℓ of vinegar was used, how many litres of water did Mark use?

Let's Practise!

10 Miss Thompson mixes blue paint and yellow paint to make green paint. When 4 buckets of blue paint and 5 buckets of yellow paint are mixed, a container of green paint is obtained.

    a Find the ratio of the number of buckets of yellow paint used to the number of buckets of blue paint used.

    b If Miss Thompson uses a total of 63 buckets of blue and yellow paint, how many buckets of blue paint does she use?

    c How many containers of green paint can Miss Thompson get if she uses 12 buckets of blue paint and 15 buckets of yellow paint?

    d How many buckets of yellow paint does Miss Thompson use if she makes 5 containers of green paint?

11 Mr Sharp used 125 g of butter, 200 g of chocolate chips and 125 g of flour to make a batch of biscuits. Mr Sharp makes 75 batches of the biscuits to sell at a charity sale. Find the:

    a ratio of the mass of butter used to that of chocolate chips used to that of flour used

    b mass of flour used, in kilograms

    c total mass of butter, chocolate chips and flour used, in kilograms.

Practice Book 6A, p.109

Let's Learn!

Word problems (2)

1 Michael and Tim had some money in the ratio 6 : 1. Michael gave half of his money to Tim. Find the ratio of the amount of money Michael had left to the amount of money Tim had in the end.

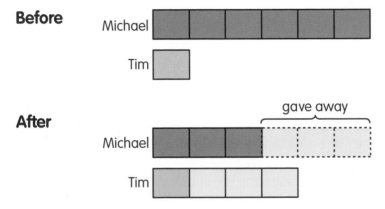

Before Michael
Tim

gave away
After Michael
Tim

The ratio of the amount of money Michael had left to the amount of money Tim had in the end is 3 : 4.

2 Mrs Lee pours some cereal into two bowls. The ratio of the mass of cereal in Bowl A to the mass of cereal in Bowl B is 9 : 5. She transfers half of the cereal from Bowl A to Bowl B. What is the new ratio of the mass of cereal in Bowl A to the mass of cereal in Bowl B?

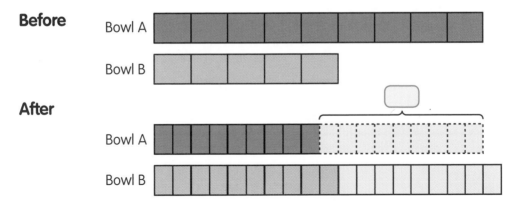

Before Bowl A
Bowl B

After Bowl A
Bowl B

The new ratio of the mass of cereal in Bowl A to the mass of cereal in Bowl B is ⬚ : ⬚.

3 Miss Phillips puts some green and blue cubes in a box. The ratio of the number of green cubes to the number of blue cubes is 2 : 1. She adds 12 more blue cubes in the box and the ratio becomes 4 : 5.

a How many green cubes are there in the box?

b How many blue cubes does Miss Phillips have in the end?

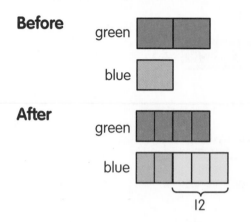

Before

green

blue

After

green

blue

12

There is no change in the number of green cubes.

The model above shows that:

a 3 units ⟶ 12 cubes

1 unit ⟶ $\frac{12}{3}$ = 4 cubes

4 units ⟶ 4 × 4 = 16 cubes

There are 16 green cubes in the box.

b 5 units ⟶ 5 × 4 = 20 cubes

Miss Phillips has 20 blue cubes in the end.

4 Saleem had some photographs of animals and plants. The ratio of the number of photographs of animals to the number of photographs of plants was 3 : 4. He took 21 more photographs of animals and the ratio became 9 : 8.

a How many photographs of plants did Saleem have?

b How many photographs of animals did Saleem have in the end?

Before

photographs of animals

photographs of plants

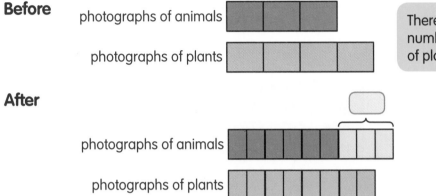

There is no change in the number of photographs of plants.

After

photographs of animals

photographs of plants

The model above shows that:

a 3 units ⟶ ☐ photographs

I unit ⟶ ☐ photographs

☐ units ⟶ ☐ photographs

Saleem had ☐ photographs of plants.

b ☐ units ⟶ ☐ photographs

Saleem had ☐ photographs of animals in the end.

5 Miss Cook and Mrs Thompson had some money in the ratio 3 : 7. After Miss Cook received £92 and Mrs Thompson received £40, both women had an equal amount of money. How much money did each woman have at first?

The model above shows that:

4 units ⟶ £92 – £40

= £52

1 unit ⟶ £$\frac{52}{4}$

= £13

3 units ⟶ 3 × £13

= £39

7 units ⟶ 7 × £13

= £91

Miss Cook had £39 and Mrs Thompson had £91 at first.

6 At the start of a game, Jack, Miya and Ruby had the same number of stars. During the game, Jack lost 12 stars to Ruby and Miya lost 20 stars to Ruby. The ratio of Jack's stars to Miya's stars became 4 : 3. How many stars did each child have at first?

Before

Jack

Miya

Ruby

After

Jack

Miya

Ruby

The model above shows that:

1 unit ⟶ ☐ stars

4 units ⟶ 4 × ☐

= ☐ stars

In the end, Jack had ☐ stars.

☐ + ☐ = ☐

Each child had ☐ stars at first.

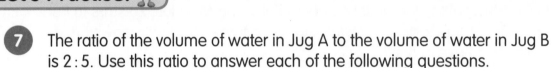

Let's Practise!

7 The ratio of the volume of water in Jug A to the volume of water in Jug B is 2 : 5. Use this ratio to answer each of the following questions.

   a If half of the water in Jug A is poured into Jug B, what is the new ratio of the volumes of water in Jug A to Jug B?

   b If half of the water in Jug B is poured into Jug A, what is the new ratio of the volumes of water in Jug A to Jug B?

   c If $\frac{1}{3}$ of the water in Jug A is poured into Jug B, what is the new ratio of the volumes of water in Jug A to Jug B?

8 A builder used cement and sand to prepare a mixture. The ratio of the number of buckets of cement to the number of buckets of sand was 1 : 2. The builder then added 8 more buckets of cement and the ratio became 5 : 2.

   a How many buckets of cement did he use at first?

   b How many buckets of sand did he use at first?

9 The ratio of the amount of money Mr Lake had to the amount of money Mr Harper had was 2 : 5. After Mr Harper's sister gave him £75 the ratio became 4 : 15. How much money did each person have at first?

10 The ratio of the number of coins Amos had to the number of coins Ethan had was 3 : 7. Ethan gave 42 coins to Amos and they ended up having the same number of coins. How many coins did each person have at first?

11 Ruby and Ella had some stickers in the ratio 2 : 3. Ella gave half of her stickers away and the ratio became 4 : 3. If Ella had given away 21 stickers, how many stickers did each child have at first?

Let's Practise!

12 There were 3 glasses containing the same volume of liquid. Mr Lee poured 210 ml of the liquid from Glass A into Glass C, and 150 ml of the liquid from Glass B into Glass C. In the end, the ratio of the volume of liquid in Glass A to the volume of liquid in Glass B was 3 : 8.

a What was the final volume of liquid in Glass A?

b What was the volume of liquid in each glass at first?

Practice Book 6A, p.113

Let's Explore!

13 The ratio of the number of beads collected by Meena to the number of beads collected by Harry is 9 : 4. Meena gave some beads to Harry.

a Find all the possible ratios of the number of beads Meena had to the number of beads Harry had, so that Meena will still have more beads than Harry after she gave Harry some beads.

b Is it possible for both Meena and Harry to have the same number of beads after Meena gave Harry some beads? Explain why.

Let's Wrap It Up!

You have learnt to:

- express one value as a fraction of another given their ratio, and vice versa
- find how many times one value is as large as another given their ratio, and vice versa
- solve word problems which involve:
  a finding one part when the ratio and the whole are given
  b finding one part or the whole when the ratio and the difference are given
  c two pairs of ratios
  d ratios in real-life situations
- use the unitary method and models to solve word problems about ratio.

Let's Wrap It Up!

Let's Revise!

14 Find the ratio of red beads to yellow beads.

red beads

yellow beads

The ratio of red beads to yellow beads is 3 : 5.

15 The ratio of Sita's age to Tom's age is 4 : 7. Express Sita's age as a fraction of Tom's age.

Sita's age is $\frac{4}{7}$ of Tom's age.

16 Tank A's volume is $\frac{5}{2}$ of Tank B's volume. Find the ratio of Tank A's volume to Tank B's volume.

The ratio of Tank A's volume to Tank B's volume is 5 : 2.

17 The mass of a bag of rice is 3 times the mass of a bag of fruit. If the mass of the bag of rice is 15 kg, what is the mass of the bag of fruit?

The mass of the bag of fruit is 5 kg.

Let's Wrap It Up!

18 Mrs Ali had 3 times as much money as Miss Murray. Mrs Ali and Miss Murray had £96 altogether.

a Find the ratio of Mrs Ali's money to Miss Murray's money.

The ratio of Mrs Ali's money to Miss Murray's money was 3 : 1.

b What fraction of the total amount of money was Mrs Ali's money?

Total amount of money = 3 + 1
$\qquad\qquad\qquad\qquad$ = 4 units

Mrs Ali's money was $\frac{3}{4}$ of the total amount of money.

c How much money did each person have?

4 units $\longrightarrow$ £96

1 unit $\longrightarrow$ £96 ÷ 4
$\qquad\qquad$ = £24

3 units $\longrightarrow$ £24 × 3
$\qquad\qquad$ = £72

Mrs Ali had £72 and Miss Murray had £24.

d How much money must Mrs Ali give to Miss Murray so that Miss Murray will have 3 times as much money as Mrs Ali?

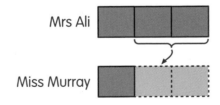

2 units $\longrightarrow$ £24 × 2 = £48

Mrs Ali must give Miss Murray £48 so that Miss Murray will have 3 times as much money as Mrs Ali.

Put On Your Thinking Caps!

19 Mrs Kim had a total of 33 watches and necklaces in her shop. After selling some watches and necklaces, she had 12 of them left. The ratio of the number of watches sold to the number of watches left was 1:2. The ratio of the number of necklaces sold to the number of necklaces that were left was 3:1. How many necklaces were there at first? Copy the table below and fill it in to solve the problem. (Hint: Make a list and solve the problem using guess and check.)

Number of Watches Sold (W1)	Number of Watches Left (W2)	W1:W2 (1:2)	Number of Necklaces Sold (N1)	Number of Necklaces Left (N2)	N1:N2 (3:1)	Total Number of Watches and Necklaces Left	Total Number of Watches and Necklaces at First
1	2	1:2	30	10	3:1	12	1 + 2 + 30 + 10 = 43

Practice Book 6A, p.119   Practice Book 6A, p.120

6 Percentage

Let's Learn!

Finding percentages

1   Let's recall.

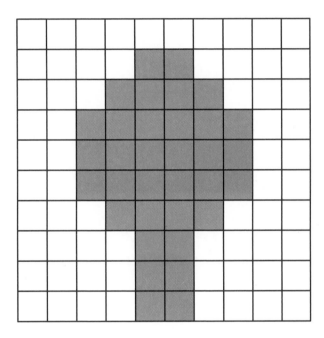

The big square is divided into 100 equal parts.
34 parts are shaded.
The shaded parts can be expressed in the following ways:

As a Fraction	As a Decimal	As a Percentage
$\dfrac{34}{100}$	0·34	34%

a Express each fraction as a percentage.

i $\dfrac{13}{20} = \dfrac{\boxed{}}{100}$

$= \boxed{}\%$

ii $\dfrac{19}{25} = \boxed{}\%$

Convert the denominator to 100.

iii $\dfrac{240}{300} = \dfrac{\boxed{}}{100}$

$= \boxed{}\%$

$300 \div 3 = 100$
$240 \div 3 = ?$

$\dfrac{3}{4} \times 100\%$

iv $\dfrac{300}{500} = \boxed{}\%$

v $\dfrac{3}{4} = \boxed{}\%$

vi $\dfrac{5}{8} = \boxed{}\%$

b Express each decimal as a percentage.

i $0{\cdot}45 = 0{\cdot}45 \times 100\%$

$= \boxed{}\%$

ii $0{\cdot}025 = \boxed{}\%$

iii $0{\cdot}08 = \boxed{}\%$

iv $0{\cdot}105 = \boxed{}\%$

c Express each percentage as a fraction in its simplest form.

i $45\% = \boxed{}$

ii $72\% = \boxed{}$

iii $8\% = \boxed{}$

iv $0{\cdot}5\% = \boxed{}$

d Express each percentage as a decimal.

i $25\% = \boxed{}$

ii $91\% = \boxed{}$

iii $4\% = \boxed{}$

iv $0{\cdot}9\% = \boxed{}$

e [calculator icon] Express each fraction as a percentage. Round your answer to the nearest whole number.

i $\dfrac{79}{120} \approx$ ⬡ %

ii $\dfrac{150}{405} \approx$ ⬡ %

iii $\dfrac{72}{303} \approx$ ⬡ %

iv $\dfrac{429}{579} \approx$ ⬡ %

2 The table shows the number of boys and girls on a school trip.

Number of boys	22
Number of girls	28
Total number of pupils	50

What percentage of the pupils on the trip are boys?

Method 1

$\dfrac{\text{Number of boys}}{\text{Total number of pupils}} = \dfrac{22}{50}$

$\dfrac{22 \times 2}{50 \times 2} = \dfrac{\boxed{}}{100}$

$= \boxed{}\,\%$

⬡ % of the pupils are boys.

Convert the denominator to 100.

Method 2

$\dfrac{\text{Number of boys}}{\text{Total number of pupils}} = \dfrac{22}{50}$

$\dfrac{22}{50} \times 100\% = 22 \times 2\%$

$= \boxed{}\,\%$

⬡ % of the pupils are boys.

Multiply by 100%.

3  George had £28. He bought a book for £15. What percentage of his money did he spend? Give your answer to I decimal place.

$$\frac{\text{Amount spent}}{\text{Total amount of money}} = \frac{\boxed{}}{28}$$

Remember to press $\boxed{C}$ before you start working on the next calculation.

$$\frac{\boxed{}}{28} \times 100\% \approx \boxed{}\%$$

He spent $\boxed{}$% of his money.

4  A cook bought 11 kg of chicken. He used 0·75 kg of the chicken on Monday. What percentage of the chicken was not used? Give your answer to I decimal place.

Amount of chicken not used = 11 − 0·75

$$= \boxed{} \text{ kg}$$

$$\frac{\text{Amount of chicken not used}}{\text{Amount of chicken bought}} = \frac{\boxed{}}{\boxed{}}$$

$$\frac{\boxed{}}{\boxed{}} \times 100\% \approx \boxed{}\%$$

$\boxed{}$% of the chicken was not used.

5 Mr Thompson had £400. He bought a jacket for £78 and spent £48 on a pair of shoes. What percentage of his money was left?

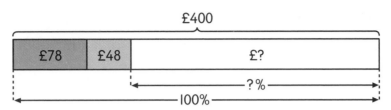

£400

£78 £48 £?

?%

100%

Amount of money left = £400 – £78 – £48

= £ ⬚

The total amount of money is 100%.

Percentage of money left = $\dfrac{\boxed{}}{\boxed{}}$ × 100%

= ⬚ %

⬚ % of his money was left.

6  The usual price of a piano was £4750. Mr Smith bought the piano at a 10% discount. He had to pay a £49·50 delivery charge on top of the sale price. What percentage of the sale price was the delivery charge? Give your answer to the nearest whole number.

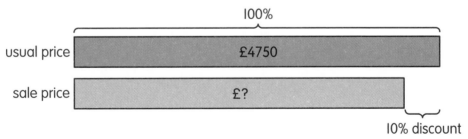

100%

usual price £4750

sale price £?

10% discount

Discount = £ ⬚

Sale price = £4750 – £ ⬚ = £ ⬚

$\dfrac{\boxed{}}{\boxed{}}$ × 100% ≈ ⬚ %

The delivery charge was ⬚ % of the sale price.

Let's Practise!

7 Express each of the following as a percentage.

    a 9 out of 100   **b** 18 out of 200

    c 165 out of 300   **d** 296 out of 400

8 Express each fraction as a percentage.

    a $\dfrac{1}{2}$ **b** $\dfrac{3}{5}$ **c** $\dfrac{7}{10}$

    d $\dfrac{32}{50}$ **e** $\dfrac{24}{25}$ **f** $\dfrac{3}{4}$

9 Express each decimal as a percentage.

    a 0·9   **b** 0·17   **c** 0·03

    d 0·028   **e** 0·005   **f** 0·104

10 Express each fraction as a percentage.

    a $\dfrac{3}{8}$ **b** $\dfrac{7}{16}$ **c** $\dfrac{28}{32}$

11 Express each percentage as a fraction.

    a 32%   **b** 5%   **c** 0·8%

12 Express each percentage as a decimal.

    a 55%   **b** 87%   **c** 7%

13 Express each fraction as a percentage. Round your answer to the nearest whole number.

    a $\dfrac{47}{86}$ **b** $\dfrac{190}{345}$

    c $\dfrac{84}{505}$ **d** $\dfrac{467}{975}$

Let's Practise!

Solve these word problems. Show your workings clearly.

14 Ruby has a ribbon 420 cm long. She uses 216 cm to decorate a present. What percentage of the ribbon is left? Give your answer to 1 decimal place.

15 A jug contained 780 ml of milk. Mrs Lee poured 221 ml of the milk into a glass and 130 ml into a cup. What percentage of milk was left in the jug?

16 The price of a poster was £4. Carl bought the poster and paid £4·80 including the delivery charge. What percentage of the original price was the delivery charge?

17 Mr Shaw puts £55 000 in a savings account. The interest rate is 3·3% per year. How much money will he have in the account after 1 year?

18 Ella spent 2 h 25 mins in a park. She spent 30 mins of the time playing football. What percentage of her time in the park was spent playing football? Round your answer to the nearest whole number.

Practice Book 6A, p.121

Let's Learn!

Word problems (I)

1 📟 15% of the children who went to a sports club wore football kits. If 30 children wore football kits, find the total number of children who went to the sports club.

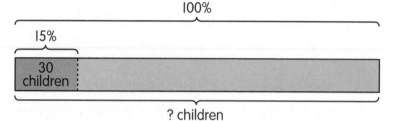

The model above shows that:

15% ⟶ 30 children

1% ⟶ 30 ÷ 15 = 2 children

100% ⟶ 100 × 2 = 200 children

> 15% of the whole is equal to 30 children.

> The whole is 100%, which is the total number of children.

200 children went to the sports club.

2 📟 Zarha got 66 marks on the maths part of her test. This was 75% of her total marks. Find the total marks for the test.

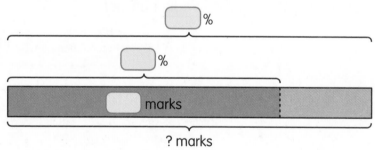

The model above shows that:

75% ⟶ ☐ marks

1% ⟶ ☐ ÷ ☐ = $\frac{☐}{☐}$ marks

100% ⟶ 100 × $\frac{☐}{☐}$ = ☐ marks

Her total mark for the test was ☐.

3 22% of Mrs Williams' monthly salary was spent on renting a house. The rental for the house was £1804 per month. What was Mrs Williams' monthly salary?

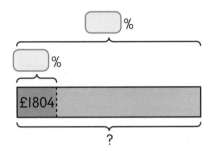

The model above shows that:

⬜% ⟶ £⬜

1% ⟶ £⬜ ÷ ⬜ = £⬜

100% ⟶ ⬜ × £⬜ = £⬜

Mrs Williams' monthly salary was £⬜.

4 Miss Knight bought a watch in a sale and she paid £40. The sale price was 20% of the original price. How much did the watch cost originally?

⬜% ⟶ £⬜

1% ⟶ £⬜ ÷ ⬜ = £⬜

100% ⟶ ⬜ × £⬜ = £⬜

The watch cost £⬜ originally.

5 Mrs Sharma put some money in a savings account. The interest was 5% of the amount of money she put in. At the end of the year, Mrs Sharma received £72·25 as interest. How much did Mrs Sharma put into the account?

⬜% ⟶ £⬜

1% ⟶ £⬜ ÷ ⬜ = £⬜

100% ⟶ ⬜ × £⬜ = £⬜

Mrs Sharma put £⬜ in the savings account.

6 Mrs Adams bought some tomatoes and paid £2·50 per kg at a market on Wednesday. On Saturday, she bought the same type of tomatoes. The price had increased by 20%. What was the price of the tomatoes per kg on Saturday?

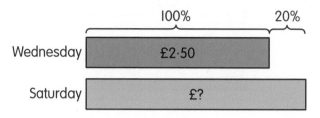

| 100% | 20% |

Wednesday | £2·50

Saturday | £?

Method I

100% ⟶ £2·50

1% ⟶ £2·50 ÷ 100 = £$\left(\frac{2\cdot50}{100}\right)$

120% ⟶ 120 × £$\left(\frac{2\cdot50}{100}\right)$

= £3

> On Saturday the price of the tomatoes was 120% of the price of the tomatoes on Wednesday.

The price of the tomatoes on Saturday was £3 per kg.

Method 2

20% of £2·50 = $\frac{20}{100}$ × £2·50

= £0·50

£2·50 + £0·50 = £3

> First find the increase in price. The increase was 20% of the price on Wednesday.

The price of the tomatoes on Saturday was £3 per kg.

7 When Jack was 9 years old, his mass was 28 kg. Two years later, his mass had increased by 30%. Find Jack's mass now he is 11 years old.

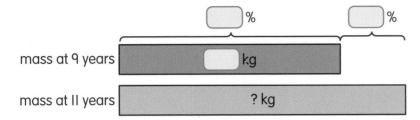

mass at 9 years

mass at 11 years

? kg

Method 1

Jack's mass when he is 11 years old is ⬚% of his mass when he was 9 years old.

100% ⟶ 28 kg

1% ⟶ 28 ÷ 100 = ⬚ kg

⬚% ⟶ ⬚ × ⬚ = ⬚ kg

Jack's mass when he is 11 years old is ⬚ kg.

Method 2

100% ⟶ 28 kg

1% ⟶ 28 ÷ 100 = ⬚ kg

30% ⟶ 30 × ⬚ = ⬚ kg

28 kg + ⬚ kg = ⬚ kg

Jack's mass when he is 11 years old is ⬚ kg.

8  The price of a new boat was £43 750 in April. However, the price of the boat was reduced by 5% in May. Find the price of the boat in May.

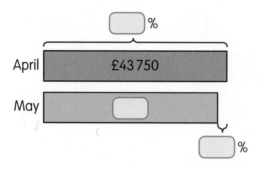

In May, the price of the boat was ⬭ % compared to the price of the boat in April.

100% ⟶ £⬭

1% ⟶ £⬭ ÷ 100 = £⬭

⬭% ⟶ £⬭ × ⬭ = £⬭

The price of the boat in May was £⬭.

9 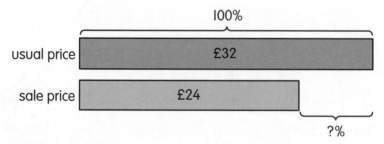 The usual price of a pair of trainers was £32. A shop sold the trainers for £24. Find the percentage discount.

£32 − £24 = £8
The discount was £8.

£32 ⟶ 100%

£1 ⟶ $\frac{100}{32}$ %

£8 ⟶ 8 × $\frac{100}{32}$ % = 25%

The percentage discount was 25%.

10 The usual price of a model aeroplane is £64. However, one shop sells the model aeroplane for £72. Find the percentage increase in price.

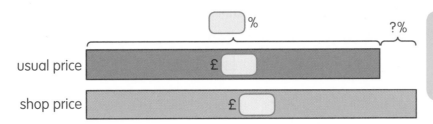

We are comparing the shop price with the usual price. We take the usual price as ( ) %.

The increase in price was £( ).

£( ) ⟶ 100%

£( ) ⟶ 8 × $\frac{\Box}{\Box}$ % = ( ) %

The percentage increase in price was ( ) %.

11 The temperature in a town was 16°C in the morning. In the afternoon, the temperature was 20°C. Find the percentage increase in temperature.

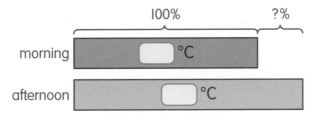

The increase in temperature was ( ) °C.

$\frac{\Box}{\Box}$ × 100% = ( ) %

The percentage increase in temperature was ( ) %.

Let's Practise!

Solve these word problems. Show your workings clearly.

12 Sophie collects UK and European coins. She has 24 UK coins. Her UK coins are 80% of her coin collection. How many coins does she collect altogether?

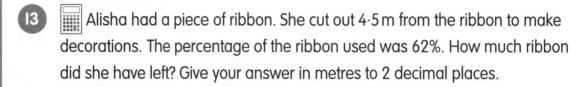

Let's Practise!

13. Alisha had a piece of ribbon. She cut out 4·5 m from the ribbon to make decorations. The percentage of the ribbon used was 62%. How much ribbon did she have left? Give your answer in metres to 2 decimal places.

14. Miss Palmer paid a total of £124·20 for a meal including 15% service charge on the cost of the meal. How much was the cost of the meal without the service charge?

15. During a sale, Mr Davies bought a digital camera for £810. This was 90% of the usual price. How much was the discount?

16. The room temperature was 24°C in the morning. Five hours later, the room temperature had increased by 12%.

    a   What was the increase in the temperature of the room to the nearest degree?
    b   What was the room temperature five hours later to the nearest degree?

17. Mrs Patel bought a fridge. When she turned on the fridge, the temperature in it was 16·2°C. After 10 hours, the temperature dropped by 75%. What was the temperature of the fridge after it had been switched on for 10 hours?

18. The sale price of 1 kg of chicken was £5·40. This was 10% less than the usual price.

    a   What was the usual price of the chicken?
    b   If the chicken was sold at a price that was 8% more than the usual price, what would be the price of the chicken?

19. The price of an entertainment system was £8999. After a year, the price of the same entertainment system was £4200. Find the percentage decrease in price. Round your answer to the nearest whole number.

20. In January, the price of a kilogram of tangerines in the supermarket was £3·20. In May, a kilogram of the same type of tangerines cost £2·99. Find the percentage decrease in price. Give your answer to 1 decimal place.

21. The price of a painting in January was £16 525. In November, the price had increased to £24 725. Find the percentage increase. Give your answer to 1 decimal place.

Practice Book 6A, p.127

Let's Learn!

Word problems (2)

1 Mr Clark paid £240 for a new suit. He had been given a 20% discount on the usual price. What was the usual price of the suit?

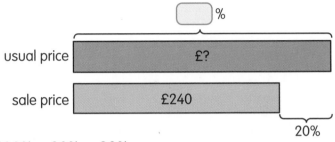

The usual price was ⬚%.

$100\% - 20\% = 80\%$
The sale price was 80% of the usual price.

$80\% \longrightarrow £240$

$1\% \longrightarrow £\left(\dfrac{240}{80}\right) = £3$

$100\% \longrightarrow 100 \times £3 = £300$

The usual price of the suit was £300.

2 A supermarket sold 75 bags of apples on Thursday. This was 40% less than the number of bags of apples that it sold on Wednesday. How many bags of apples did the supermarket sell on Wednesday?

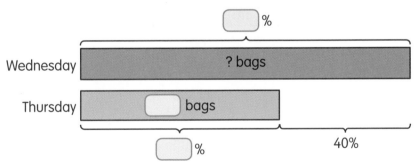

The number of bags of apples the supermarket sold on Thursday is ⬚% of the number of bags that it sold on Wednesday.

⬚% $\longrightarrow$ ⬚ bags

$1\% \longrightarrow \dfrac{⬚}{⬚} =$ ⬚ bags

$100\% \longrightarrow 100 \times$ ⬚ $=$ ⬚ bags

The supermarket sold ⬚ bags of apples on Wednesday.

3 Mr Ward had a piece of leather. He cut off 30% of the piece of leather to make a belt. The remaining length of the piece of leather was 385 cm long. He then cut off 25% of the remaining piece of leather to make a necklace.

a What was the original length of the piece of leather?

b What was the remaining length of the piece of leather after he made the necklace?

a

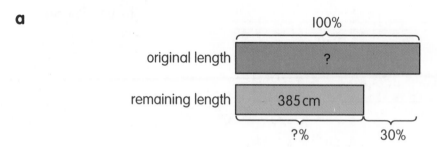

$100\% - 30\% = 70\%$

$70\% \longrightarrow 385\,cm$

$1\% \longrightarrow 385 \div 70 = 5{\cdot}5\,cm$

$100\% \longrightarrow 100 \times 5{\cdot}5 = 550\,cm$

The original length of the piece of leather was 550 cm.

b

$100\% - 25\% = 75\%$

$75\% \times 385 = 288{\cdot}75$

The remaining length of the piece of leather after he made the necklace was 288·75 cm.

4 A flask of hot water was left to cool. After 10 minutes, the temperature had decreased by 24% to 76°C. After another 5 minutes, the temperature of the water decreased by another 20%.

    a What was the original temperature of the water in the flask?

    b What was the final temperature after 15 minutes?

a

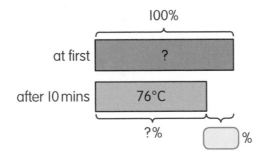

100% − ⬭% = ⬭%

⬭% ⟶ ⬭°C

1% ⟶ ⬭ ÷ ⬭ = ⬭°C

100% ⟶ 100 × ⬭ = ⬭°C

The original temperature was ⬭°C.

b

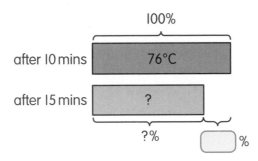

100% − ⬭% = ⬭%

⬭% × 76°C = ⬭°C

The final temperature after 15 minutes was ⬭°C.

5 In 2014, Mr Hall's monthly salary was £2000. Mr Brook's monthly salary was $\frac{4}{5}$ of Mr Hall's monthly salary. In 2015, Mr Brook's monthly salary was increased by 20%. Find the increase in Mr Brook's monthly salary.

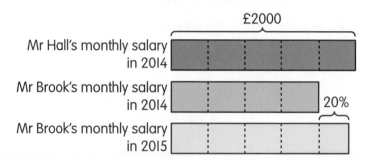

£2000

Mr Hall's monthly salary in 2014

Mr Brook's monthly salary in 2014

Mr Brook's monthly salary in 2015

20%

Mr Brook's monthly salary in 2014 $= \frac{4}{5} \times$ £2000

$=$ £1600

100% ⟶ £1600

1% ⟶ £1600 ÷ 100 = £16

20% ⟶ 20 × £16 = £320

We are comparing Mr Brook's monthly salary in 2014 with his monthly salary in 2015. So we take his monthly salary in 2014 as 100%.

The increase in Mr Brook's monthly salary was £320.

6 In May Mr Phillips bought 12 kg of potatoes and Mrs Shaw bought $\frac{5}{4}$ as many potatoes as Mr Phillips. In June Mrs Shaw bought 30% more potatoes than she bought in May. Find the increase in the mass of potatoes Mrs Shaw bought in June.

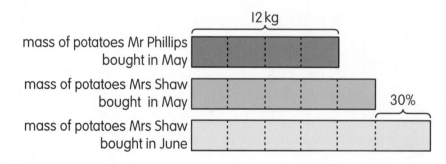

12 kg

mass of potatoes Mr Phillips bought in May

mass of potatoes Mrs Shaw bought in May

mass of potatoes Mrs Shaw bought in June

30%

Mass of potatoes Mrs Shaw bought in May = $\dfrac{5}{4} \times 12$

= $\boxed{}$ kg

100% ⟶ $\boxed{}$ kg

1% ⟶ $\dfrac{\boxed{}}{100}$ kg

We take the mass of potatoes Mrs Shaw bought in May as 100%.

30% ⟶ $30 \times \dfrac{\boxed{}}{100} = \boxed{}\dfrac{\boxed{}}{\boxed{}}$ kg

The increase in the mass of potatoes Mrs Shaw bought in June was $\boxed{}\dfrac{\boxed{}}{\boxed{}}$ kg.

7 Matt had an orange ribbon and a blue ribbon. The orange ribbon was 2 m long. The blue ribbon was $\dfrac{4}{5}$ as long as the orange ribbon. Matt cut 25% off the blue ribbon.

a What was the length of the blue ribbon before it was cut?

b Find the length of blue ribbon that Matt cut off.

a

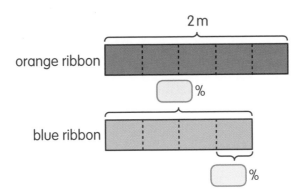

$\dfrac{4}{5} \times 2 = \boxed{}$

The blue ribbon was $\boxed{}$ m long before it was cut.

b $25\% \times 1 \cdot 6 = \boxed{}$

Matt cut $\boxed{}$ m of the blue ribbon.

8 The usual price of a model car in 2011 was £12. In 2013, the price of the model car increased to £15. In 2015, the price of the model car was £3 more than the price of the model car in 2013.

    a   Find the percentage increase in the price of the model car from 2011 to 2013.

    b   Find the percentage increase in the price of the model car from 2013 to 2015.

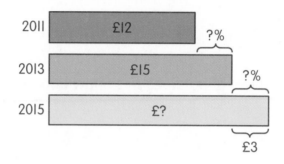

a   Increase in price of model car from 2011 to 2013 = £15 − £12

$$= £3$$

Percentage increase = $\dfrac{3}{12} \times 100\%$

$$= 25\%$$

The percentage increase in the price of the model car from 2011 to 2013 was 25%.

b   Percentage increase in price = $\dfrac{3}{15} \times 100\%$

$$= 20\%$$

The percentage increase in the price of the model car from 2013 to 2015 was 20%.

> We are comparing the price of the model car in 2013 with the price of the model car in 2015. So we take the price of the model car in 2013 as 100%.

9 The temperature of the water in a mug was 50°C at first. After 10 minutes, it dropped to 45°C. Another 15 minutes later, the temperature had dropped to 40°C.

a Find the percentage decrease in temperature after the first 10 minutes.

b What was the percentage decrease in temperature from 45°C to 40°C? Give your answer to 1 decimal place.

at first | 50°C

after 10 mins | 45°C | ?%

after 25 mins | 40°C | ?%

a Decrease in temperature = 50°C – 45°C

$$= \boxed{}°C$$

$$\frac{\boxed{}}{\boxed{}} \times 100\% = \boxed{}\%$$

The percentage decrease in temperature after the first 10 minutes was $\boxed{}$%.

b Decrease in temperature = 45°C – 40°C

$$= \boxed{}°C$$

$$\frac{\boxed{}}{\boxed{}} \times 100\% \approx \boxed{}\%$$

The percentage decrease in temperature from 45°C to 40°C was $\boxed{}$%.

10 Mr Smith raised money for charity by walking for three days across the countryside. He raised £925 on the first day. On the second day, he raised £728. By the third day he had raised a total of £2538.

a What was the percentage decrease in the amount of money raised from the first day to the second day? Give your answer to 1 decimal place.

b Find the percentage increase or decrease in the amount raised from the second day to the third day. Give your answer to 1 decimal place.

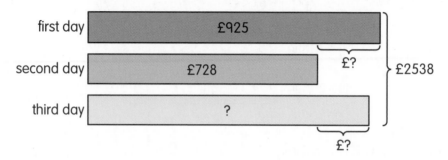

a Decrease in amount of money raised = £925 – £728

= £ ☐

Percentage decrease = $\dfrac{\square}{925}$ × 100%

≈ ☐ %

The percentage decrease in the amount of money raised from the first day to the second day was ☐ %.

b Amount raised on the third day = £2538 – £925 – £728

= £ ☐

☐ in amount of money raised = £ ☐ – £ ☐

= £ ☐

Percentage ☐ = $\dfrac{\square}{728}$ × 100%

≈ ☐ %

The percentage ☐ in the amount of money raised from the second day to the third day was ☐ %.

Maths Journal

11 Miya and Hardeep worked out the following:

In an experiment, a scientist had to record the temperature change of some liquid in a flask. The temperature of the liquid in the flask was 50°C at first. After 10 minutes, the temperature of the liquid dropped to 40°C. Another 20 minutes later, the temperature of the liquid had dropped to 30°C.

Find the percentage decrease in temperature from 40°C to 30°C.

Miya's answer:
40°C − 30°C = 10°C

$\frac{10}{50} \times 100\% = 20\%$

The percentage decrease in temperature was 20%.

Hardeep's answer:
40°C − 30°C = 10°C

$\frac{10}{40} \times 100\% = 25\%$

The percentage decrease in temperature was 25%.

a Whose answer is incorrect?

b Explain why.

Let's Practise!

12 Mrs Baker paid £120 for a suitcase. She had been given a discount of 20% on the usual price. What was the usual price of the suitcase?

13 In 2014, the number of subscribers for Magazine A was 475 and the number of subscribers for Magazine B was $\frac{4}{5}$ of the number of subscribers for Magazine A. In 2015, the number of subscribers for Magazine B increased by 35%. Find the total number of subscribers for Magazine B in 2015.

14 Ishani had 20 cards. Emma had $\frac{7}{2}$ of the number of cards Ishani had. Emma gave 25 cards to her friends. Find the percentage decrease in the number of cards Emma had. Give your answer to 2 decimal places.

15 The temperature at noon in Delhi was 32°C. In the evening, it had dropped to 28°C. At midnight, the temperature was 24°C.

    a Find the percentage decrease in temperature from noon to evening.

    b Find the percentage decrease in temperature from evening to midnight. Give your answer to 2 decimal places.

16 Mr Bell put £10 000 into a savings account. At the end of the first year, the amount of money in the account had increased to £10 450. At the end of the second year, he had £10 900 in the savings account.

    a Find the percentage increase in his money at the end of the first year.

    b Find the percentage increase in his money from the end of the first year to the end of the second year. Give your answer to 1 decimal place.

Practice Book 6A, p.133

Let's Wrap It Up!

You have learnt to:

- find the whole given a part and the percentage
- find a part given the whole and the percentage of the other part
- solve word problems by finding percentage increase and percentage decrease
- solve word problems involving percentage and discount.

Let's Revise!

17 During a sale, Mrs Green paid £176 for an oven at a discount of 12%. What was the usual price of the oven?

12%

sale price | £176

usual price | £?

$100\% - 12\% = 88\%$

The sale price was 88% of the usual price.

88% ⟶ £176
1%   ⟶ £2
100% ⟶ £200

The usual price of the oven was £200.

Let's Wrap It Up!

18 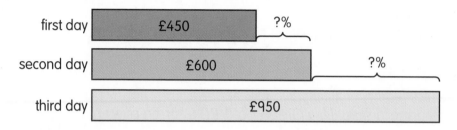 A charity raised money by selling raffle tickets. It raised £450 on the first day. On the second day it raised £600. On the third day, the charity raised £950.

first day | £450 | ?%
second day | £600 | ?%
third day | £950

a What was the percentage increase in the amount of money raised from the first day to the second day? Give your answer to 1 decimal place.

Increase in amount of money raised = £600 − £450
= £150

Percentage increase = $\frac{150}{450} \times 100\%$
$\approx 33 \cdot 3\%$

The percentage increase in the amount of money raised from the first day to the second day was 33·3%.

b Find the percentage increase in the amount raised from the second day to the third day. Give your answer to 1 decimal place.

Increase in amount of money raised = £950 − £600
= £350

Percentage increase = $\frac{350}{600} \times 100\%$
$\approx 58 \cdot 3\%$

The percentage increase in the amount of money raised from the second day to the third day was 58·3%.

Put On Your Thinking Caps!

19 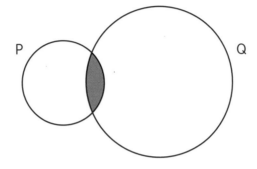 In the diagram below, the area of the shaded part is 30% of the area of Circle P. It is also 20% of the area of Circle Q. What percentage of the diagram is shaded? Give your answer to 2 decimal places. (Hint: Find the ratio of the area of the shaded part to the unshaded part of each circle.)

P   Q

Practice Book 6A, p.141   Practice Book 6A, p.144

© 2015 Marshall Cavendish Education Pte Ltd

Published by Marshall Cavendish Education
Times Centre, 1 New Industrial Road, Singapore 536196
Customer Service Hotline: (65) 6213 9444
Email: tmesales@mceducation.com
Website: www.mceducation.com

Distributed by
Oxford University Press
Great Clarendon Street, Oxford,
OX2 6DP, United Kingdom
www.oxfordprimary.co.uk
www.oxfordowl.co.uk

First published 2015

ISBN 978-981-01-8904-4

Printed in China

Acknowledgements
Written by Dr Fong Ho Kheong, Gan Kee Soon and Chelvi Ramakrishnan

UK consultants: Carole Skinner, Simon d'Angelo and Elizabeth Gibbs

Cover artwork by Daron Parton

The authors and publisher would like to thank all schools and individuals
who helped to trial and review Inspire Maths resources.